Photo by J. Carver Harris

Castillo de San Marcos at St. Augustine, Florida

The English Siege of 1702 gave this Spanish fort its baptism of fire. The cannon is part of the Spanish 16-pounder which was overcharged and blew up during the siege.

THE SIEGE OF ST. AUGUSTINE IN 1702

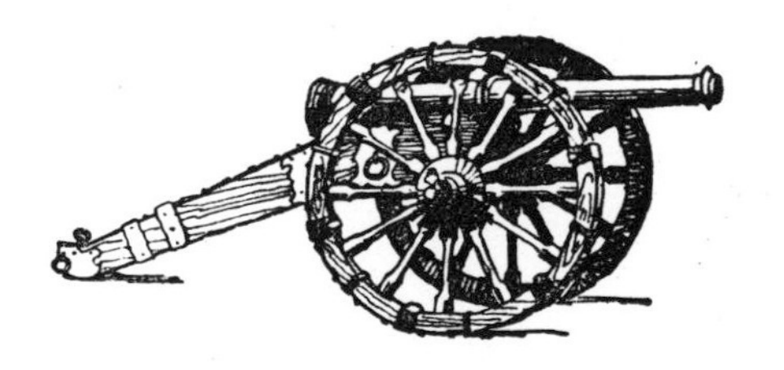

BY
CHARLES W. ARNADE

Published in cooperation with the

ST. AUGUSTINE HISTORICAL SOCIETY

UNIVERSITY OF FLORIDA PRESS

Gainesville

1959

The text of this volume was originally published by the University of Florida Press as No. 3 of the University's Social Sciences Monograph Series. This series is sponsored by the Graduate School of the University of Florida and is directed by an Editorial Committee composed of the following members:

Library of Congress
Catalogue Card No. 59-63743

PRINTED BY THE RECORD PRESS
ST. AUGUSTINE, FLORIDA

ACKNOWLEDGMENTS

Research for this monograph was made possible by a generous grant from the St. Augustine Historical Society. The grant enabled me to dedicate a full two months in the summer of 1958 to research and writing. Mr. J. Carver Harris, Mrs. Doris Wiles, Mr. J. T. Van Campen, Mr. X. L. Pellicer, Mrs. Max Kettner, Mrs. Luis Arana, and Mr. William Griffen of the Society were helpful at various times. Mr. Albert Manucy, Mr. Luis Arana, and Mr. Ray Vinten of the United States National Park Service (which today administers Castillo de San Marcos National Monument, the historic fort that is so much a part of this narrative) gave valuable technical and scholarly help. Professors Hale Smith, Charles Fairbanks, Benjamin Rogers of Florida State University, and Donald Worcester, Lyle McAlister, Rembert Patrick, John Mahon, Curtis Wilgus, John Goggin, and Ripley Bullen of the University of Florida offered valuable advice. A special word of thanks goes to Mr. Julien C. Yonge and Miss Margaret Chapman of the P. K. Yonge Library of Florida History for their help and for making many facilities available to me. Dr. Mark Boyd of Tallahassee, Mr. David True of Miami, and Mr. Edward Lawson of St. Augustine at one time or another were extremely helpful. My wife, Marjorie, as usual had the tedious chore of typing the various drafts. To these friends, and especially to the St. Augustine Historical Society, many thanks. Naturally I assume full responsibility for the content of the monograph.

CHARLES W. ARNADE

GAINESVILLE, FLORIDA
SEPTEMBER, 1959

CONTENTS

ILLUSTRATIONS

1. FLORIDA AND CAROLINA AROUND 1700

In 1670 a new English colony had come into existence on the North American continent. Its first colonists came from England and Barbados and called their new home Carolina. They established their towns and plantations in territory claimed exclusively by Spain as part of Florida. Although Spanish hegemony in the Carolina land was hardly perceivable since the Spanish frontier had been withdrawn to the south, the very soil on which the first Carolinians stepped was historical ground where once the Spanish banner proudly flew. The famous Pedro Menéndez de Avilés had personally established forts and outposts in Carolina a century before the English arrival. Overextension, lack of gold and precious metals, apathy, ferocious Indians, maladministration, jealousies, and other causes forced the Spanish to retreat toward St. Augustine and Apalachee. Carolina and north Georgia as well as Alabama remained Spanish only in name and on paper.

The settlers of Carolina, imbued by a restless energy, a religious fervor, a shrewd business instinct, and a hatred for Catholic Spain, were determined to remain and expand. This they did. In all directions, but especially west and south, the pioneers and traders of Carolina blazed the trail. The forceful story of this chapter of American colonial history has been written with scholarly pen by Professor Verner Crane in his study *The Southern Frontier* (*11*)*, today a classic of American history. The men of Carolina, according to the Spaniards, were living, moving, and expanding on Spanish soil. Surely a controversy, if not war, was in the making over the "debatable land," a phrase employed by Professor Herbert Bolton (*6*).

For more than thirty years an undeclared war was waged in this disputed land with Guale, or eastern Georgia, as the main battleground. Spain's efforts to eradicate English Carolina from St. Augustine were complete failures. Many natives flocked to the English side, the side which had more goods to offer. Those Indians who remained loyal to Spain were eagerly considered slave material by the Carolina plantation owners. Therefore raiding parties by the English and their Indian allies forced the Spaniards to fall back farther south. One Spanish governor

*Citations throughout refer to the numbered items in the Bibliography.

after another requested help to destroy the English menace, but nothing was forthcoming. One positive action was undertaken, however, when St. Augustine was made a main bastion for Spanish defense of the Atlantic. A massive stone fort, the dream of every governor since Menéndez de Avilés, became a reality. It was started in 1672, and by the end of the century the fort at St. Augustine was the strongest and largest on the continent this side of Veracruz (*17*). The stage was set for a larger English-Spanish engagement. International events slowly led to its fulfillment.

France's ownership of the best waterways of North America was yet incomplete without sovereignty over the Mississippi, especially its mouth. By the end of the seventeenth century, just when Carolina was expanding, France decided to act since Spain had neglected the Gulf coast. By 1700 France had achieved her purpose and Louisiana was in the making. The Spanish crown, wishing to forestall the French, occupied Pensacola Bay and in this way a new area of conflict was created. Furthermore, while Carolinians gained at the expense of Spain in east Georgia, their more enterprising traders were moving west, approaching the Mississippi. Another regional clash was shaping up. The outlook was for a triangular struggle over the Southeast.

To the Carolinians the main enemy had been Spain ever since the creation of their province. This was most natural as they had intruded on soil claimed by Spain, and they were living "in the very chaps of the Spaniard" (*11*, p. 3, n. 1). At the same time they were disdainful of the Spaniards, sure that Spain's forced exit from North America was just a matter of time. The Carolinians underestimated the strength and might of Spain; they had a more healthy respect for the French. France was the mightiest nation in Europe with a great colony in North America. Although removed from the battlefield of King William's War (1689-1697), Carolina knew that England had failed to eject France from Canada. Both countries had fought to a stalemate in America. In Carolina France's power was overestimated. The news of the establishment of Louisiana meant that Carolina traders going west would meet with Frenchmen moving north and east, and this was considered a serious matter. The Spanish danger was relegated to a secondary position. The struggle for the Mississippi, in which Carolina would play a vital role, surged to the forefront. But a sudden new international development in Europe brought about a shift in the triangular picture of the North American Southeast.

In 1700 the European nations changed their alliances. The king of Spain had died without successor. Powerful King Louis XIV of France claimed the throne for his Bourbon grandson. The other European nations were unwilling to see Spain and France united under one crown, and an international war seemed likely. The war clouds soon reached English North America, causing great consternation. Spain and France united would mean nearly total encirclement. In Carolina the dismay was even greater. Professor Crane tells us "that the more timid settlers talked of removal to safer regions" (*10*, p. 383) should the union of the two crowns become a reality. To be sure, the majority of the Carolinians who had braved the elements of nature, Indians, and Spaniards were unwilling to give up so easily. Nevertheless anxiety lay over the aggressive Protestant colony.

The governor of Louisiana had already formulated a plan to stop the English advance westward and to strike at the Atlantic coast via Spanish Florida in a combined allied offensive. St. Augustine would serve as the main base for this flank attack. Spain would recover the debatable land, with French help, and in return would turn Pensacola over to Louisiana. Although the plan was only on paper, a fancy of the French governor and one which apparently failed to arouse the Spaniards to equal enthusiasm, it did make sense. More than one intelligent and far-sighted Carolinian must have pondered the possibility of a combined French-Spanish offensive in the west, from the southeast, and by the waters of the Atlantic. If war came in Europe over the Spanish succession, such an attack was quite probable. A sturdy hand was needed in Carolina to guide the province through the coming times.

In September, 1700, James Moore, an outspoken colonist, "ambitious and impecunious planter" (*11*, p. 40), "active, ambitious and aggressive high-churchman" (*28*, p. 157), and ruthless slave dealer, became governor of Carolina. Serious research has yet to sketch his true personality. Professor Crane considers him an important man who played a "great role in the creation of the southern frontier and of provincial western policy" (*11*, p. 40). He was unquestionably intelligent, but also reckless. Moore understood the forthcoming international danger. He feared and respected the French and despised and underestimated the Spaniards. The new governor was aware of the danger that the union of the two crowns would mean. He had heard of the great Spanish fort and garrison at St. Augustine. It was his opinion that if war came, the English of Carolina must strike at St. Augustine before it became an allied base.

If St. Augustine were to be reinforced by French troops and equipment the survival of Carolina would be seriously endangered. He tried to convince public opinion in favor of war policies.

In May, 1702, the Proprietors in England sent word to Carolina of the beginning of the War of the Spanish Succession, known in American history as Queen Anne's War. By August the official news had not yet reached Charleston, but Governor Moore had advance intelligence of the war's outbreak. On August 20, 1702, he urged on the Carolina Commons "the takeing of St. Augustine before it be strengthened with french forses" (*23*, p. 64). At first the Commons refused to grant permission for the St. Augustine expedition but rather favored defensive measures. On August 26 the official news of the outbreak of the war reached Carolina and the Commons looked with more favor on Moore's proposal. By early September the legislative body authorized the offensive. Enthusiasm prevailed in the colony and the Assembly proclaimed "the Encouragement to free Plunder and a share of all Slaves" (*23*, p. 84). It also announced that "all persons that go on this expedition shall have an equal share of all plunder" (*28*, p. 163). Thereupon the legislature appropriated two thousand pounds sterling for expenses. In this way was born the Moore attack on St. Augustine, a vital battle in Spanish Florida history.

The Assembly had estimated that the expedition should have at least 350 white men, of which the majority should be transported in six or more vessels. It calculated that attack on St. Augustine could be terminated victoriously in two months. Because of this the body appropriated seven hundred pounds of the two thousand in salaries for the men, each man receiving ten pounds a month besides an "equal share of plunder" (*23*, p. 85). The Commons House of Assembly on August 28 thought that Colonel Robert Daniel, Lieutenant Colonel George Dearsley, Major Will Smith, Captains James Risbee, William Davis, and others were "fitt to be Commanders on the present Expedition." Some of these men indeed turned up in the attack on St. Augustine. There was some sentiment in the House to appoint Colonel Robert Daniel commander of the expedition, but the question "carried in the negative" (*23*, p. 84). It was resolved that Governor Moore would be commander-in-chief. The members wrote Moore that "having turned our eyes round about us we can find no person so very capable as your Honor." The Carolinian representatives thought that by giving the job to Moore they could not "in the least doubt of all imaginable success" (*23*, p. 86). Moore said

"that nothing but delay can make me doubt of Success" (*23,* p. 92). In another act during the same month the House ordered "that all vessels be imbargoed" (*23,* p. 83). In all, the Commons House of Assembly had acceded readily to Governor Moore. Once convinced of the feasibility of an offensive the legislators gathered momentum in being cooperative. By September Moore was ready to move south.

The printed English sources about the St. Augustine expedition are sparse and somewhat contradictory. In summary this is what happened: David Ramsay states that about 500 provincial militiamen together with some 300 Indians, mostly Yamasees, made up the expeditionary force which gathered at Port Royal, the "fixed place of rendezvous" (*21,* p. 127). John Oldmixon tells us that "the Number of Men which were enlisted for this Enterprise were 1,200, 600 English and 600 Indians" (*19,* p. 342). Michael Cole reports "five hundred men and three hundred Indians sayled from hence about ye 16 October" (*97*). Fourteen boats, mostly confiscated from private sources, were available to transport the men south. A very simple plan of operation was adopted. Colonel Robert Daniel approached St. Augustine by a land route; Commander Moore attacked the Spanish presidio by sea and blocked the harbor with part of his fleet. The route to St. Augustine was a victorious one and several Spanish outposts along the coast were destroyed. According to Oldmixon, Colonel Robert Daniel, "a very brave Man," marched on St. Augustine "up the River in Periagas and came upon Augustino on the land side, while the Governor sail'd thither and attacked it by Sea. . . . Col. Daniel in his way took St. John's, a small Spanish settlement; as also St. Mary's, another little village, belonging to the Spaniards. After which he proceeded to Augustino, came before the Town, enter'd and took it; Col. Moor not being yet arrived with the Fleet" (*19,* pp. 342-343). The city of St. Augustine was easily captured and the English soldiers marvelled at the riches of the town, with its large church and comfortable Franciscan friary. But the English land and sea forces occupied only an empty town. The garrison and inhabitants had retreated into St. Augustine's formidable citadel, the Castillo de San Marcos.

The conquest of St. Augustine and Florida without the capture of this fort would indeed have been an empty victory. Governor Moore decided to take it, but discovered that he lacked the necessary artillery. He therefore dispatched Colonel Daniel to Jamaica to bring siege cannon, bombs, and mortars. In the meanwhile Moore laid siege to the

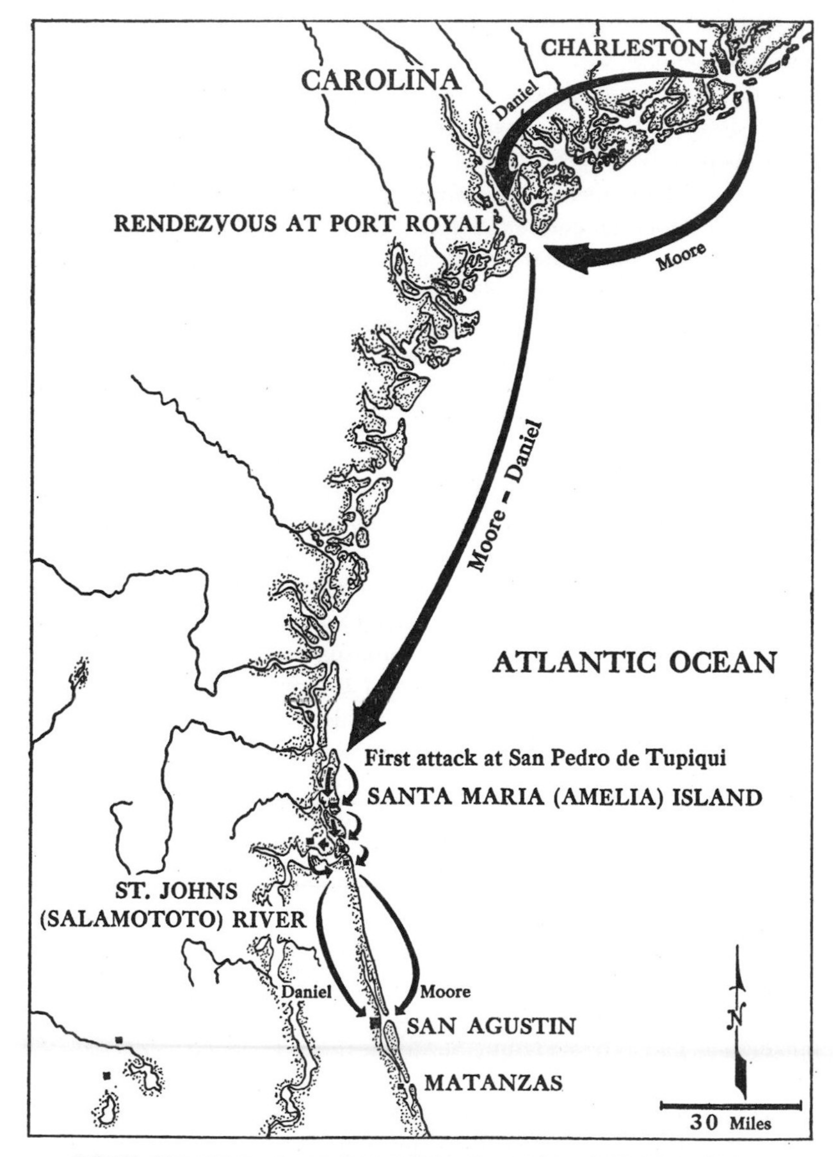

THE ENGLISH ADVANCE ON ST. AUGUSTINE
OCTOBER-NOVEMBER, 1702

fort, hoping that he might induce the surrender of the garrison by starvation. The Spaniards inside the castle showed endurance and strength, and the reinforcements from Jamaica failed to arrive. The morale of the Carolina force began to crumble after a two-month siege. Then suddenly, without advance intelligence, two large Spanish ships with heavy guns arrived from Havana and "bottled up" (*11*, p. 77) the eight English vessels. Oldmixon insists that the two Spanish ships were "two small Frigats, one of 22, and the other of 16 guns" (*19*, p. 344). According to John Ash, Moore "resolved bravely to put on Board his Eight Vessels then riding in the Harbour all their Goods and Plunder, and with his few men about 500, Fight thro' the Enemy, and so come Home. But the Pillow, which often let out Heat to make way for Caution, changed this his Resolution" (*4*, p. 272). Seeing his precarious situation, Governor Moore set fire to his cornered fleet and retreated hastily by land 40 miles north to the mouth of the St. Johns. Here he embarked his tired men in his relief ships and returned to Carolina. Oldmixon tells us that "Arratommakaw, King of the Yanioseaves [Yamasees?], who commanded the Indians, retreated to the Periagas [Piragua=small, shallow-draft vessel] with the rest, and there slept upon his Oars, with a great deal of Bravery and Unconcern. The Governor's Soldiers taking false Alarm, and thinking the Spaniards were coming, did not like this slow Pace of the Indian King in his Flight; and to quicken him in it, bad him make more Haste: But he reply'd, No; tho your Governour leaves you, I will not stir till I have seen all my Men before me" (*19*, p. 344).

The expedition had been a failure from the over-all point of view. The powerful fort, or *castillo,* was not conquered and consequently Spanish Florida continued to exist. The cost of the campaign went far beyond the appropriated 2,000 pounds, costing exactly 8,495 pounds, 14 s., 9d. (*28*, p. 163; *24*, pp. 87-92 and pp. 126-127). Professor Crane says that consequently Carolina "entered upon the evil course of paper-money issue" (*11*, p. 77). Governor Moore became thoroughly discredited. The Carolina House voted him thanks "for his Courage and Conduct" but the powerful Mr. John Ash dissented because "he thinks the General much wanting in his conduct particularly in not using his power to punish disobedient and cowardly officers to which in a great measure he [Ash] thinks our ill success may be imputed" (*24*, p. 25). John Archdale, in his survey of Carolina written in 1707, said that Moore's adventure in St. Augustine "was ready to make a Mutiny among

the People; for many Vessels had been press'd to that Service, which being burn'd by the Governour's order, because they should not fall into the Spaniard's Hands, the Masters demanded Satisfaction; and an Assembly being call'd, great Debates and Divisions arose, which, like a Flame, grew greater and greater" (*3*, p. 313).

Furthermore, Moore and Captain Daniel and some of his officers were openly accused of having kept the rich plunder and ignoring the law that had promised free plunder and an equal share of it (*24*, pp. 86, 126). The failure of the St. Augustine siege encouraged further attempts to destroy Spanish Florida. Although ending in partial success, it did not achieve the desired goal of eliminating Spain from southeast North America. The march on St. Augustine of 1702 had a few positive features. Moore and his legions had destroyed the garrisons of Amelia Island and therefore "forced the Spanish frontier to fall back another step" (*6*, p. 60). Although the expedition was costly in funds and ships, Moore's army lost only two lives. Taken by surprise when the Spanish reinforcements appeared in the harbor, the governor was able to maneuver his army out of enemy country. One of Governor Moore's personal political enemies, John Ash, had to admit that Moore "retreated with such caution and dispatch, that he lost not one man by the enemy" (*4*, p. 273). Carolinians had learned that Spanish Florida was not an easy prey and that the Spaniards had still plenty of initiative. In summary, the siege of St. Augustine in 1702 was one of the first large engagements in the international struggle on the North American continent, a dispute that would assume vast proportions as the eighteenth century progressed. This particular engagement was more than a raid for plunder, but rather marked the beginning of a century of warfare in North America.

☆ ☆ ☆

The position of Florida in 1702 and the years preceding was fairly adequate, if compared with a century before. By 1600 Spanish Florida claimed all of North America east of New Mexico, although in reality only St. Augustine and a few missions on the southern Georgia coastal islands were inhabited by the Spaniards. St. Augustine itself was a miserable place with a rotting wooden fort. By 1700, a hundred years later, Spain's Florida claimed less territory, but the inhabited places over which the Spanish banner flew had grown in number. In the west,

Pensacola had come into existence as the second largest Spanish community of Florida. In between lay the rich region of Apalachee with abundant natives and Spanish missions, with its center in today's Tallahassee. A considerable cattle-growing region with Spanish creole ranchers from St. Augustine was flourishing in Timucua, with today's Gainesville area as its focal point. By 1700 the Georgia missions, which had achieved their maximum growth by the mid-seventeenth century, had been severely decimated by the English. Even so, they continued their existence around Amelia Island. South Florida remained unoccupied by the Spanish. But the St. Johns, Suwanee, Santa Fe, and St. Marks rivers were Spanish waterways. The presidio of St. Augustine, still an undesirable place compared with other towns in the Americas, had improved considerably. The massive fort dominating the city gave it stature and prestige. A spacious church and beautiful Franciscan friary added to the decorum. Professor John R. Dunkle, studying the birth records, estimates the number of inhabitants of the town at 912 in 1701 (*12,* p. 8). The real size of the population of Florida remains a matter of speculation.

The most precise census is one from the year 1689 when the Bishop of Cuba sent the crown a list of Florida *doctrinas* (Indian parishes under the supervision of a priest) with their number of native families. Florida was divided into four provinces. Guale with six *doctrinas* had a total of 185 families. Timucua had thirteen *doctrinas* with 591 families. Apalachee, the most prosperous of the Florida provinces, was also listed with thirteen *doctrinas* containing 1,920 families. The fourth province was identified as "Provincia Nueba" and was unquestionably located in south Florida. It contained only two villages with 100 families. The total for the four provinces was 2,796 families, and it was estimated that each family was composed of five people, making a total of 13,980. In addition, the city of St. Augustine was listed as having 500 families or 1,444 people, including whites, Indians, and Negroes (*31*).

From this census it can be seen that the families in St. Augustine did not measure up to the ratio of five to a family indicated by the bishop. This was because St. Augustine was a strictly military town. The whole life of the place gravitated around the fort. According to law the garrison for the protection of all of Florida was to be 355 men strong. Most of these men by 1700 were *criollos* from St. Augustine and could be classified as local boys. Even so, the city with its extremely low birth rate (due to the lack of women) could not satisfy the demand

for the full quota of 355. Requests by the governors to bring the garrison up to full strength are of common occurrence in the archives. In 1699 the garrison was composed of eighteen staff officers, of which two were on pension. It had 254 men in the infantry, divided into three companies. Of these, 30 men were incapacitated for one or another reason. The artillery was composed of 18 men, one of whom was permanently sick. The navy had 23 able men. There were two full-time Indian interpreters. This gives a total of 315 men on the payroll, which was 40 short of the required quota. But of the 315 men, 33 were either on pension or incapacitated. Thus, in 1699 Florida had a military garrison of only 282 able-bodied men to guard the vast area that composed the four provinces (*32*).

By 1702, the year of the Moore attack, the number of the garrison had risen to 323, of which 25 were listed as pensioned or incapacitated because of age or sickness. These men who faced the Moore offensive were organized and distributed in the following manner. First was the governor, supreme commander of Florida, who was not included in the 355-man quota. He held extensive military, executive, legislative, judicial, and administrative power. Two royal officials, the treasurer and the accountant, shared the administrative power with the governor; they too were not part of the garrison quota. The main military figure was the sergeant major. He was the troop commander, directly responsible to the governor and who in case of vacancy of the governorship assumed that position until the new governor arrived. Below him were listed the three captains of the three infantry companies. The infantry also had three ensigns, three sergeants, twelve corporals, six drummers, three fifers, and three pages. The artillery had only one captain and nineteen artillerymen. Besides these there were fifteen more staff or administrative officers, including a military accountant, a customs official, the commander of the fort who had four adjutants, two foremen who watched the slaves and convicts, two scribes, an armorer, a blacksmith, a barber (physician), and an apothecary. Part of the garrison were the two Indian interpreters who were conversant in the languages of Guale, Apalachee, and Timucua. One hundred and thirty-seven infantry soldiers were stationed in St. Augustine, living in the fort which they and the artillerymen guarded twenty-four hours a day. Thirty soldiers and an officer were stationed in Apalachee, especially in the Tallahassee region. They were the soldiers farthest removed from St. Augustine. In 1702 twelve infantrymen and one officer guarded Guale, with

their headquarters on Amelia Island. In the province of Timucua there were only three soldiers stationed in the Gainesville-Lake Santa Fe region. Two soldiers were located on the crossing of the Salamototo [St. Johns] River that led from St. Augustine to Timucua and Apalachee. These two men maintained contact with the small Timucua garrison. The various sentinel posts around St. Augustine required 25 men. The navy had fifteen sailors and a pilot in charge of the small vessels that belonged to the *presidio.* All these men, including the incapacitated and pensioned and excluding the governor and two royal officials, came to 323. This made the garrison 32 men below the 355-man quota. In fact, the effective fighting force of Florida, exclusive of Pensacola, which was not considered part of the provinces, was only 298. The actual strength at St. Augustine, including the sentinel posts, was 249 professional soldiers and officers, plus the governor and the two royal officials (*33*). This was the force that must defeat Governor Moore and his attacking army.

The first news the Spanish governor of Florida, Joseph de Zúñiga y Zerda, had about the approaching attack of Governor Moore came from a baptized Indian woman of the Chacato tribe (*30,* fol. 3280). She had gone from Apalachee to the lands of the Apalachicolas in today's western Georgia, a region which had fallen under the influence of the English traders from Carolina. At the village of Achito in Apalachicola, the native woman had attended a town council in which plans were being discussed for an English-inspired and -supervised attack on Spanish Apalachee. The Chacato woman subsequently witnessed some war preparations by the Apalachicolas. Being devoted to the Spaniards, she fled to San Luis de Apalachee (today's Tallahassee), where she arrived on the afternoon of October 21, to report the news. Immediately she talked to Captain Juan Solana, the Spanish commander of Apalachee, and Captain Francisco Romo de Uriza, who had recently arrived from St. Augustine with reinforcements. Among other things, the Chacato Indian told the two captains the amazing news that the governor of "San Jorge," which was the Spanish name for Charleston, would come down the Atlantic coast with as many as a hundred small boats to attack St. Augustine. The next day, October 22, Solana and Romo de Uriza forwarded the news to St. Augustine by a speedy messenger who arrived at the fort five days later (*34, 35*).

Governor Zúñiga was quite worried about this news and thought it credible, though perhaps exaggerated. He issued a proclamation on

October 27 telling the garrison and people of St. Augustine about the Chacato information. Zúñiga asked them to take the news seriously and said that although he had continually asked for help from Spain, Havana, Pensacola, and French Mobile, he could expect no immediate aid. Under these circumstances the presidio and garrison must be mobilized and put on twenty-four-hour notice. Zúñiga gave orders that beginning October 28 no inhabitant of St. Augustine be allowed to leave the town premises without express permission of the governor. All reserve soldiers and officers were called into active duty; all leaves were canceled. The garrison was ordered to check and clean weapons and have them ready for a moment's notice (*36*). The governor was an energetic man of great administrative talents, who had had twenty-eight years of dedicated service to the crown, including war service in Africa and Flanders. He was taking no chances since he was well aware of the aggressiveness of the English. He was also cognizant of the military weakness of his garrison in terms of men and arms.

On November 1 the worried governor again wrote an urgent letter to the crown, outlining his extremely weak position. He was short of men and ammunition to defend the vast provinces of Florida which the English from Carolina were determined to conquer. Zúñiga identified Florida as being composed of Apalachee, Timucua, "La Rinconada, Bay of Tanpa known as La Ascensión, the coast of Carlos, that of the South, Tororo, and Mayaca." All these places the correspondent identified as having inhabitants, Apalachee and Timucua possessing the

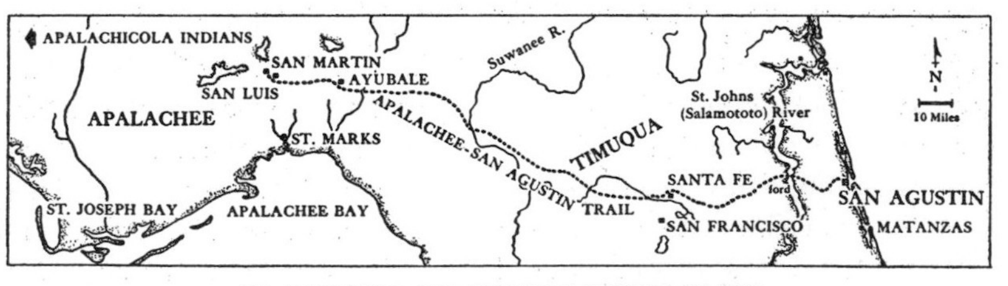

ST. AUGUSTINE AND WESTERN FLORIDA IN 1702

heaviest concentration. The morale of the Indians from these two provinces, composed of four thousand Christians plus infidels such as the "Sabacolas, Chacates, Tabosas or Catases, Pacanas, Amacanas, and other nations," was at a low point. The English goal was to wean Indian allegiance away from the Spaniards and conquer St. Augustine and the

fort, and thereby gain control of the Bahama Channel, a vital Spanish route. The executive wanted one hundred more soldiers from Spain and fifty from Cuba, plus weapons and ammunition. Furthermore, Zúñiga again reminded the crown that Spain's goal in the Atlantic must be to destroy Carolina, once and forever. Since time was of the essence, he said he was ordering the sloop from Havana, which was in the port of Apalachee, and the frigate "La Gloria" of the St. Augustine presidio, to sail to Pensacola and French Mobile to request aid (*37*).

On the same day the royal officials, with the governor's approval, wrote a similar letter to the governor and royal officials of Havana. The immediate need was reinforcements to defend St. Augustine from the English. The final goal should and must be a counteroffensive. They said that "the depopulation and expulsion of these Englishmen from San Jorge is urgent. This can easily be done, because they have no fort or any other defenses." St. Augustine offered its full cooperation in the expedition which was recommended for "this spring" (*39*).

By November 1 the governor and the administrative officers of St. Augustine were sure of an English attack but had little intelligence information. A third letter was sent to Solana, the lieutenant governor of Apalachee. He was instructed to question the Chacato woman again, and speed any further developments to St. Augustine. He was also warned to be prepared for an attack by the English and their Indian allies. Even though material was short at the presidio, some hoes and axes were ready to be dispatched to Solana for the purpose of erecting a blockhouse. It is presumed that this wooden structure, "with a palisade big enough to hold sufficient people" was to be located at San Luis. Captain Solana was ordered to soothe the various Indian chiefs. The Havana sloop, anchored at St. Marks, must be confiscated and sent to Pensacola for aid. This drastic action was adopted by consent of the war council of all staff officers. Due compensation must be offered her captain and crew for their work. Should the crew resist the order, Solana was to put the men under arrest and replace them with experienced Apalachee soldiers. Captain Jacinto Roque was assigned the task of taking the request for aid to Pensacola, and Solana was to assign Roque the soldiers needed to fulfill the order. Zúñiga informed Solana that he was dispatching the royal frigate of the St. Augustine garrison to Havana for further aid. Nicolás Monsón carried the governor's instructions to Apalachee on the royal trail, arriving at San Luis several days later (*38, 76*).

2. THE ENGLISH APPROACH

While Zúñiga was sending south and west for help the English were approaching St. Augustine from the north, entering into Spanish-held territory by the beginning of November. They began their assault on Guale at midnight of November 3. The Carolina army surprised the guardhouse of San Pedro Bar at Santa María Island (Amelia) which overlooked the water that separated it from San Pedro Island (Cumberland). The two Spanish guards, Domingo Gonzales and Juan Tejada, died defending their post. Immediately afterward the attackers overran the native village of San Pedro de Tupiqui, which presumably was on the northern part of the island. Some of the Christian Indians were able to flee south to the missions and villages of San Felipe and Santa María located on the same island. These two places were close together; one was the administrative center of Guale and had a wooden fort with a strong palisade. In it lived Captain Francisco Fuentes de Galarza, the lieutenant governor of Guale, with his attractive and pregnant wife, their three charming daughters, and one small son. It was said that another daughter of Fuentes, voluptuous and beautiful, had an illicit relationship with Governor Zúñiga in St. Augustine and for this reason the governor had removed the father and mother to Guale (*30*, fols. 3209-3207).

At one o'clock in the morning of November 4 the fleeing Indians from the northern part of the island arrived at the stockade, reporting the unexpected English invasion to Fuentes de Galarza. The captain and the two Franciscan friars, Manuel de Urissa and Domingo Santos, immediately rang the church bells, alerting the people to the oncoming attack and asking them to defend the stockade, the mission, and the villages. Instead, panic broke out among the neophytes and spread to all the natives, who began to flee the island or hide in the woods and swamps. Fuentes de Galarza and the friars tried desperately to calm the Indians, but their companions from San Pedro de Tupiqui had spread exaggerated tales of English atrocities. The lieutenant governor reported that with his few soldiers he was unable to stop the fleeing Indians as the native leaders were unable or unwilling to cooperate.

Consequently the captain ordered complete evacuation of the fort, mission, and island. He and the friars collected the church ornaments

and statues. Just at this moment the English arrived and showered the fort and mission with burning spears which fell on the palmetto roofs. At once flames engulfed the structures, lighting the dark night of the island. Apparently everyone got out, including the soldiers, the commander, and the friars. They fled to the next important Spanish outposts of San Juan del Puerto on Fort George Island, the Indian village of Santa Cruz on the mainland across from the western shore of the island, and to the stockade and mission of Piribiriba located just across from the island on the southern shore of the Salamototo River, near today's Mayport. Captain Fuentes arrived at San Juan del Puerto, the last outpost of Guale, in the late afternoon of November 4. He immediately rushed the grave news to the governor in St. Augustine (*40, 41, 44*).

Governor Zúñiga received the dispatch at noon on November 5. It told him of capture of Amelia Island by the English and the retreat to San Juan del Puerto "located twelve leagues from the presidio." Captain Fuentes de Galarza reported that the Carolina force was composed of "English, Indian, and Negro soldiers." Zúñiga, aware that his fears had come true, thought it of prime importance to hold San Juan del Puerto, which he considered as "the key to the province of Guale." It was also the outer defense line of St. Augustine. And "if the enemy capture it, they can come overland and besiege the fort," thought the governor. Therefore he commissioned Captain Joseph de Horruytiner, who was in charge of the guards at the fort and lookout posts, to take twenty infantrymen to reinforce the decimated army of Captain Fuentes de Galarza, and defend San Juan del Puerto and the crossing of the Salamototo River. Horruytiner's force left immediately (*44*).

In another order of the day all men, including "free Negroes and Mulattoes," over fourteen years who were not part of the garrison, were ordered to go to the fort within one hour to receive arms and ammunition. This militia was put on a twenty-four-hour alert. No inhabitants were allowed to leave the town limits and a fine of two hundred *ducados* was declared for infractions of the orders of the day, to be deducted from the accumulated salary debts owed to each one. A fine of two hundred lashes was assigned for delinquent St. Augustinians classified as free persons of color (*pardos* and *morenos*) (*41*). Also, all farmers were ordered to bring their produce, especially corn, and deposit it inside the fort within twenty-four hours. It was to be handed over to the commander of the fort, who must measure it and give a signed receipt to the farmers. Every family was allowed to draw out

THE ENGLISH ADVANCE ON

OCTOBER-NOVEMBEI

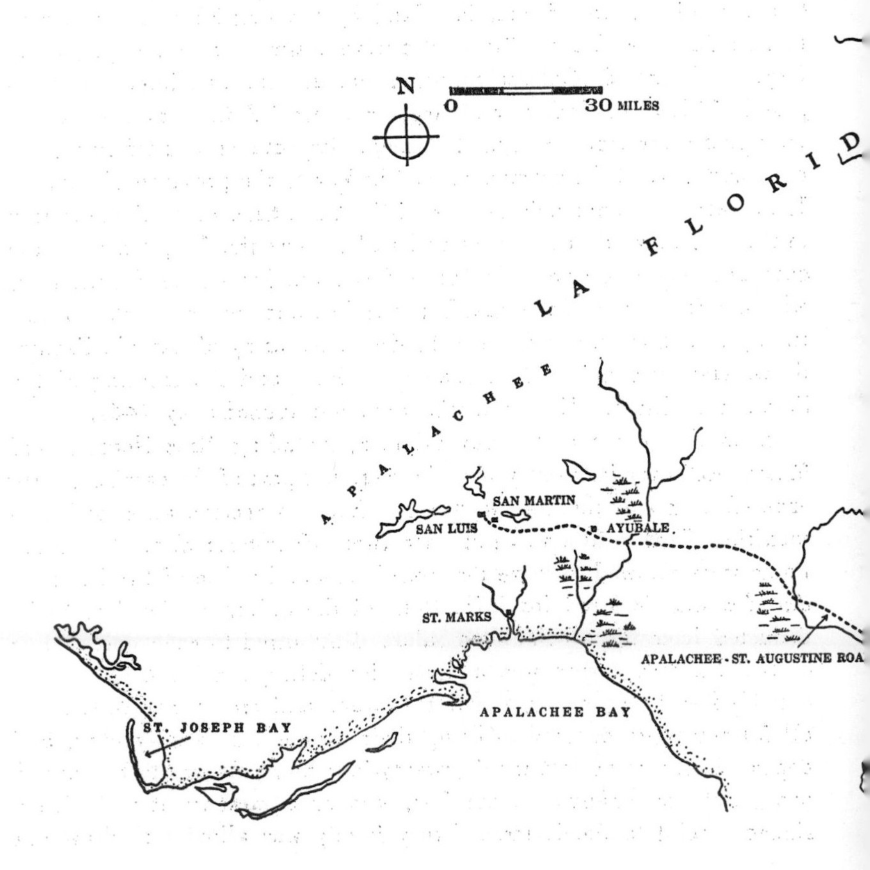

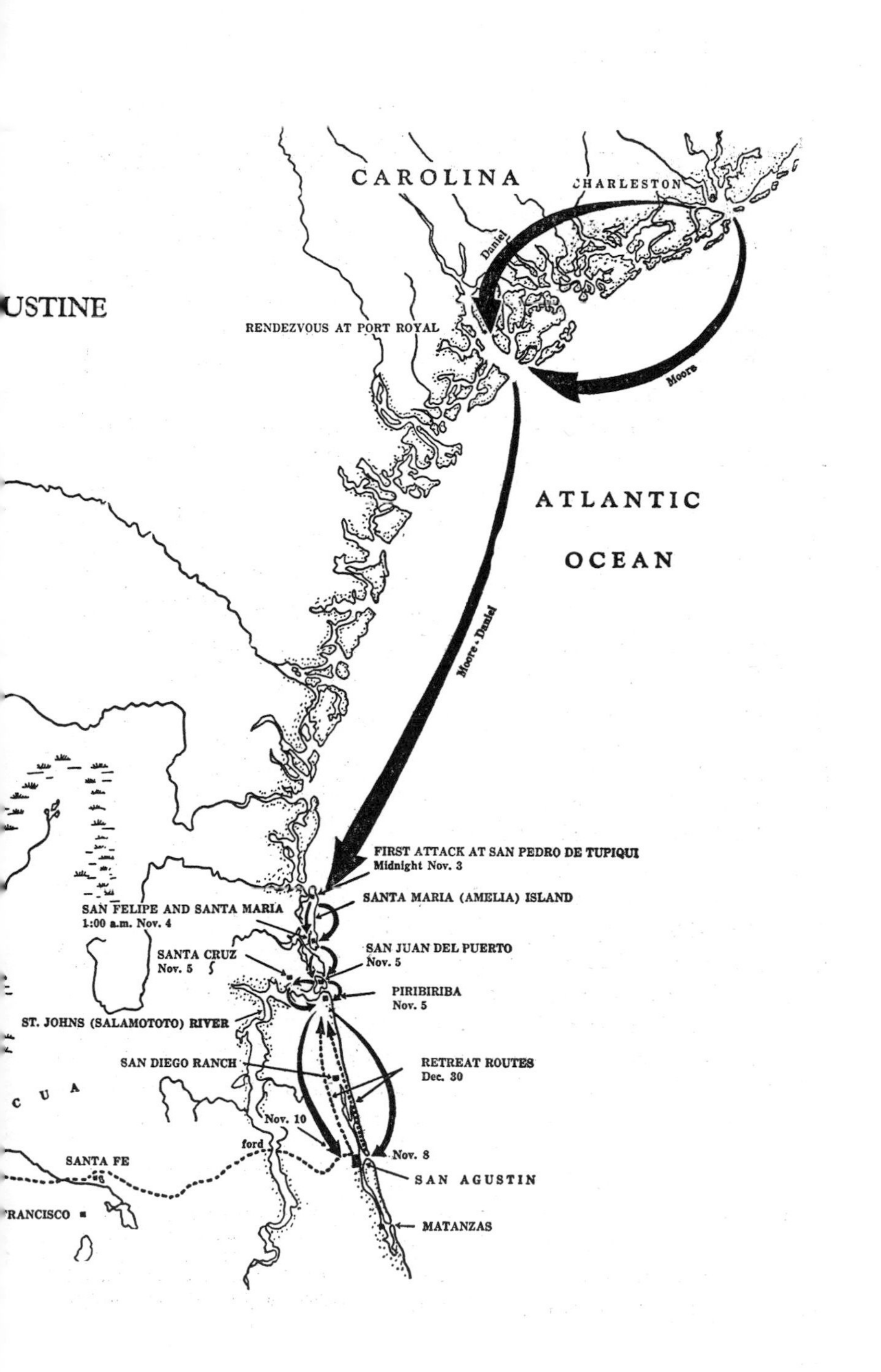
USTINE
CAROLINA
CHARLESTON
Daniel
Moore
RENDEZVOUS AT PORT ROYAL
ATLANTIC
OCEAN
Moore - Daniel
FIRST ATTACK AT SAN PEDRO DE TUPIQUI
Midnight Nov. 3
SANTA MARIA (AMELIA) ISLAND
SAN FELIPE AND SANTA MARIA
1:00 a.m. Nov. 4
SAN JUAN DEL PUERTO
Nov. 5
SANTA CRUZ
Nov. 5
PIRIBIRIBA
Nov. 5
ST. JOHNS (SALAMOTOTO) RIVER
SAN DIEGO RANCH
RETREAT ROUTES
Dec. 30
C U A
Nov. 10
ford
SANTA FE
Nov. 8
SAN AGUSTIN
RANCISCO
MATANZAS

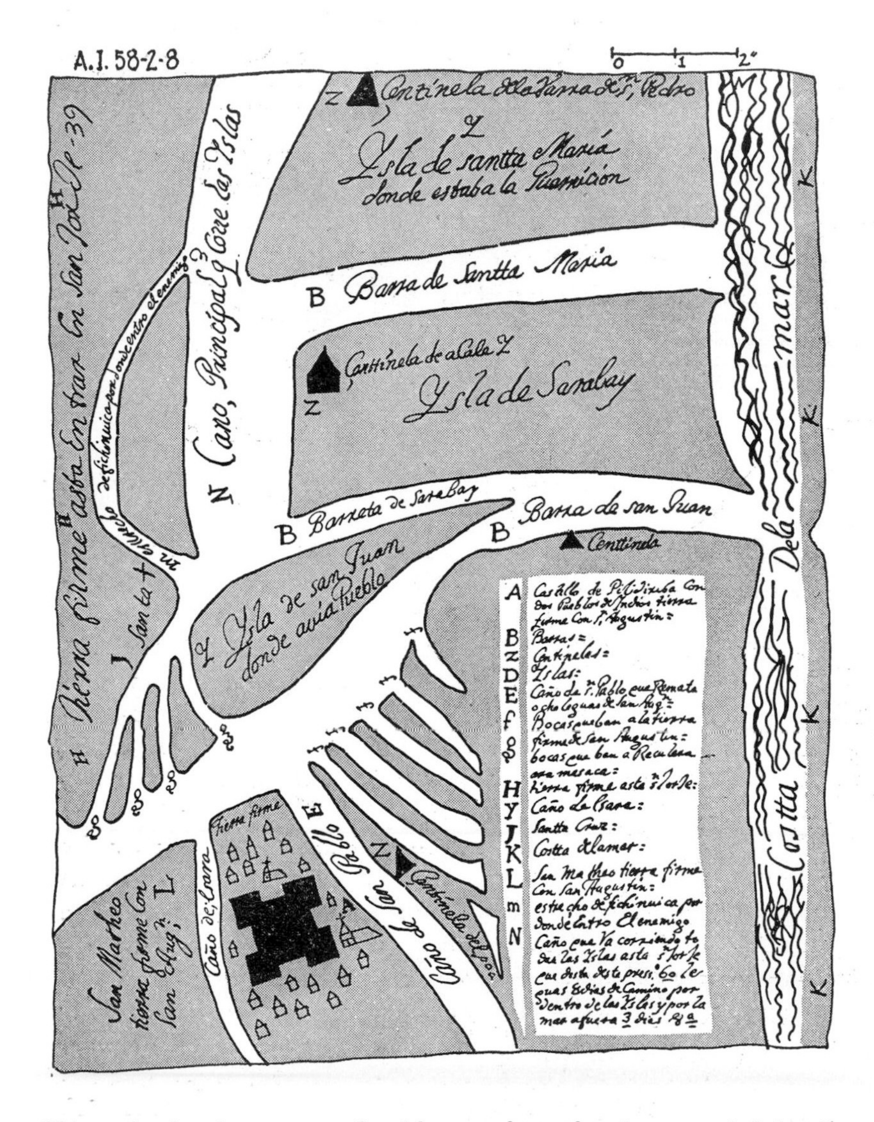

This undated and anonymous Spanish map shows the places attacked by the English near the St. Johns River on the approach to St. Augustine. The illustration is a line facsimile, from a photocopy of the original wash drawing [AI 58-2-8]. Note that Little Talbot Island, the southerly third of which is an accretion since colonial times, is shown as one with Big Talbot (Sarabay). Note also that D of the key is on the map as Y. The facsimile omits illegible words, as the names of the two shore lookouts near B and E, and a phrase written in the narrow space between *Costta* and the key.

Translation of the Key

A—Fort of Piribiriba and two Indian villages, on the mainland with San Agustín.
B—Bars.
Z—Lookouts.
D—Islands.
E—San Pablo Creek, which ends eight leagues from San Agustín.
f—Mouths [of creeks] that lead into the San Agustín mainland.
g—Mouths [of creeks] which end at Aramasaca.
H Mainland to San Jorge [Charleston].
Y—Sara Creek.
J—Santa Cruz.
K—Seacoast.
L—San Mateo, on the mainland with San Agustín.
m—Fichinuica Channel, through which the enemy came.
N—Channel which runs along all the islands up to San Jorge [Charleston], which is 60 leagues from this presidio, eight days' travel by the island waterway and three days by open sea, &c.

Place Names on the Map Which Are Not Identified in the Key

Lookout for San Pedro [St. Marys River] Bar.
Santa María [Amelia] Island, where the garrison was.
Santa María [Nassau River] Bar.
Acale Lookout.
Sarabay [Talbot] Island.
Sarabay [Fort George River] Bar (small).
San Juan [St. Johns River] Bar.
San Juan [Fort George] Island, where there was a village.

the corn needed daily, but an exact written account must be kept of each transaction. Any infraction of this last order must be presented to the governor, who would impose a fine according to his pleasure (*43*).

Planning on the possibility that the English assault might be delayed on the St. Johns by Fuentes de Galarza and Horruytiner while the Spanish cautiously retired into the fort for a siege, the governor, treasurer, and auditor talked about sending another request for help to Havana by the royal frigate. They decided to tell of the conquest of Amelia Island and state that the English were advancing rapidly toward St. Augustine. "Because of the lack of men, arms, and ammunition," they went on, "we are forced to close ourselves in the fort as soon as the enemy arrives." Not only did they fear the English, but they considered the possibility that some of the Indians might take the opportunity to rebel, and they recited the obligation to "protect the holy images, ornaments, jewels of the Church, the clergy, friars, people of the environs, women, and children." Immediate aid by sea was requested. A naval task force was thought to be more advisable because it would help to lift any siege that the English imposed with the Carolina army. A second choice of at least two hundred infantrymen was listed. A further request was the sending of twenty soldiers with the royal St. Augustine frigate to bolster the garrison of Apalachee. All these demands were considered urgent since other help, especially from the west, was considered beyond the realm of possibility and the presidio's ammunition was too low for a sustained siege. Zúñiga and the royal officials agreed that the frigate "La Gloria" under Captain Alonso Alvarez should carry the message, since it was equipped and ready to sail. No officer of the fort could be spared as official messenger, but the governor suggested the appointment of Fray Francisco Camacho, who was considered an able and conscientious man. It was decided to request the permission for Camacho's appointment from the Franciscan superior, Fray Marcos de Sotolongo. Alonso Alvarez would informally contact the authorities of Havana and also present St. Augustine's plight (*45, 47*).

Just after supper a messenger arrived from the sentinel post at San Juan del Puerto, twelve leagues from St. Augustine, saying that three English sails had been sighted. At nine, Zúñiga ordered the alarm sounded and sent every man to his station for alternate watches (*46*). Then, at the end of this eventful day, November 5, 1702, Governor

Zúñiga decided to write one more letter to the crown before retiring for the night. He was incensed at the present plight of Florida and St. Augustine, which he blamed on the negligence of the viceroy in Mexico and the executive officers of Havana. Consistently they had ignored requests for reinforcements and the talk about a counteroffensive "to throw out the enemy from San Jorge." Even though the enemy was at the gates of the fort, thoughts about a Spanish attack on Carolina should not be abandoned. Zúñiga offered full cooperation in this venture and suggested St. Augustine as the base for the invasion. The king was asked to increase the garrison "by 250 men in order to bring it up to six hundred" and to send fifty new recruits every two years in order to maintain the roster. With the present garrison it was impossible to guard the vast expanse of Florida, since it was eighty leagues to Apalachee, thirty leagues to Timucua, and twenty-five leagues to Guale. It was the governor's opinion that the English had dared to attack because they knew that Florida was short of armed forces (*44*).

At two in the morning the governor was awakened by the arrival of another messenger from the Salamototo estuary, sent by Captain Horruytiner. The man reported that a Carolinian sloop had landed a launch, and the Spanish forces had captured three men, two English soldiers, and "one Indian of the Chiluque nation." The Indian was cooperative when interrogated by the Guale interpreter and declared that "the governor of San Jorge is advancing personally with many vessels and many men by land and sea in order to conquer the fort and town of St. Augustine." Several hours later more discouraging news arrived at the fort. The English appeared to have crossed the Salamototo successfully, taking San Juan del Puerto, Piribiriba, and Santa Cruz. The exact happenings along the estuary remain unknown, for Captain Horruytiner was never able to establish full contact with the Guale force. The panic of the Santa María Island Indians fleeing southward had spread to the Indians of the three estuary villages and facilitated their rapid capture. The twenty soldiers of the San Juan del Puerto stockade and the few at Piribiriba were routed and some were captured by the English. Captain Fuentes, accompanied by the two Franciscan fathers, was able to cross the river, still carrying the church ornaments. He wanted to regroup the men and offer resistance on the south side of the river, but his army disintegrated and he had to flee into the "woods, swamps, and palmettos" with his family. Thus he was unable to gather the fifty men he needed to harass the enemy. The captain praised the courage

and enterprise of the two friars, who were, incidentally, later captured by the English and sent to Charleston. Fuentes was unable to send a messenger to St. Augustine until the end of November, keeping the governor completely in the dark about the Spanish troops in Guale (*46*, *87*). On an undetermined date the captain and his family were also captured and taken to Charleston where his wife delivered their next child (*24*, p. 51).

Although the news was disjointed, it was obvious that the English had surmounted the last obstacle before attacking St. Augustine. Consequently, on the morning of November 6 Zúñiga decided to issue a frank proclamation to his army and the people of St. Augustine. He told them of the retreat of the Guale army under Fuentes and its defeat at Santa María Island and at the Salamototo River because of superior English forces. The governor told his people that "the enemy is approaching by land and by sea and they are bringing the means to attack and besiege the royal fort." It was stated that there was a genuine fear that the loyalty of some Indians was questionable, and the Carolina forces would take advantage of this. Some natives who were well informed about conditions in St. Augustine might rush to the English forces, and tell them "everything about this town, its streets, entrances, environs, creeks, bars, tidelands, paths to the cattle and other ranches, savannas, and other places." The proclamation did not hide the deficient situation of the garrison. Especially bad was the status of the infantry, which since 1687 had not received a recruit from the outside. Zúñiga reminded the people that he and his predecessors had tried many times to remedy this situation but were ignored by higher authorities. He had finally dispatched the popular and extremely capable Captain Juan de Ayala y Escobar to Spain, but he had not yet returned. Furthermore no provisions had arrived at St. Augustine for the last three months; there was a shortage of everything.

The governor announced that he was going to order everyone inside the fort. This meant all the inhabitants of St. Augustine and the environs, including friars, priests, women, children, Negro slaves, free Negroes, and "all Indians of whatever nation which have rendered obedience to his Catholic Majesty." Zúñiga estimated it would bring into the fort about 1,500 to 1,600 persons. Most of these people were "poor as a churchmouse"; for a long time the garrison's only pay had been "two breads a day," so it would be the responsibility of the authorities to feed everyone inside the fort. This would be a most difficult task. But

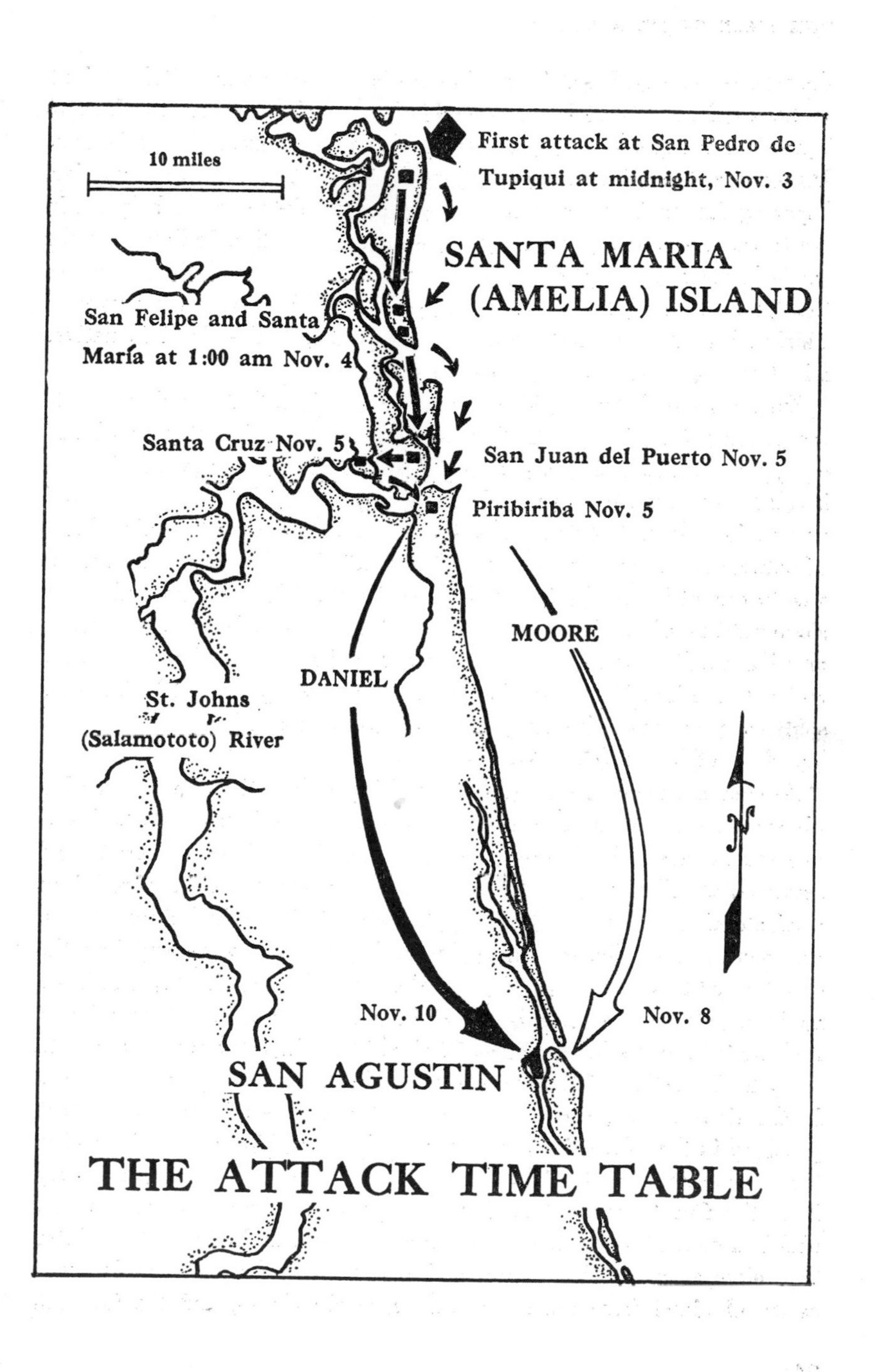
10 miles
First attack at San Pedro de Tupiqui at midnight, Nov. 3
SANTA MARIA (AMELIA) ISLAND
San Felipe and Santa María at 1:00 am Nov. 4
Santa Cruz Nov. 5
San Juan del Puerto Nov. 5
Piribiriba Nov. 5
MOORE
DANIEL
St. Johns (Salamototo) River
Nov. 10
Nov. 8
SAN AGUSTIN
THE ATTACK TIME TABLE

the people were told that it was imperative for everyone to take refuge in the castle. It would be completely demoralizing for the garrison to leave their families outside, exposed to English capture. It would be only human that the garrison would then be hesitant to return enemy fire, knowing that their wives, children, and other relatives were helpless in the town. It was also good policy to send the Christian Indians into the castle because the English might unleash the heathen Indians, such as the "Jororo, Tucuime, and Aypaje," who would butcher their converted Florida brethren. Besides, if left outside the fort, the Catholic natives might return to their old savage customs.

Zúñiga warned the inhabitants and his garrison that the siege would last a long time, for two basic reasons. One, their infantry was badly equipped, besides being understaffed and made up partly of old and invalid men plus inexperienced young boys. Second, the enemy would unquestionably find on the ranches near St. Augustine "an abundance of cattle, corn, beans, and other provisions." Therefore the correct move was to retreat inside the fort and force the English to a long and costly siege until reinforcements arrived from "Apalachee, Mobile, Pensacola, and Havana," to which urgent messages had been sent for men, arms, and ammunition. He ended his proclamation by saying that he gave his soldiers' promise to the king that they would defend the castle to the last drop of blood (*46, 54*).

As soon as the governor had released his proclamation, he commanded his sergeant major to announce the order to move into the fort. Everyone must come with his movable belongings including his "jewels and ornaments." The priests, friars, and administrators of the religious confraternities were told to bring the church items including statues, ornaments, and bells. Indian guides and translators were sent into the countryside to bring the natives to the fort where their stay would be made as pleasant as possible, "although the Indians, Negroes, and mulattoes have no belongings to bring." The infantry was ordered to carry to the castle "all the shingles possible that are being manufactured in the treasury house and the ones that have been imported and are piled up in the *plaza de armas* to roof the parochial church." Another task was to remove "the planking [*tablazón*] of the church" and carry it to the fort to make "lodging and quarters where the women and children could find refuge . . . against the cold and rain of the winter that always comes rigorously during these months." Permission was easily obtained from the sacristan, Sebastián Groso, and the foreman

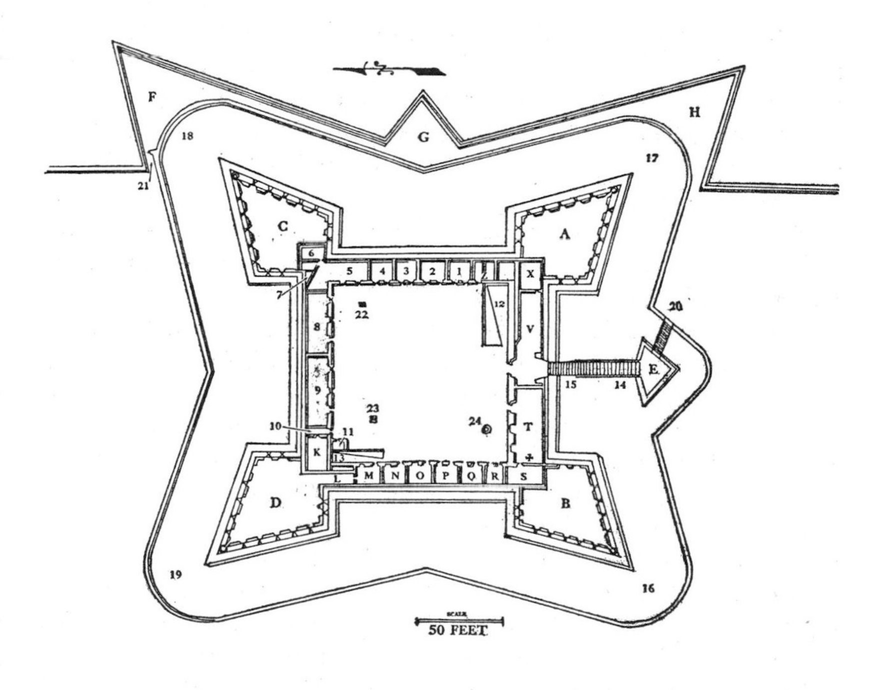

PLAN OF THE FORT

The plan, although drawn in 1737 by Antonio de Arredondo, represents the fort substantially as it was in 1702. In this facsimile, important items from the key are translated below.

A. San Agustín bastion
B. San Pedro bastion
C. San Carlos bastion
D. San Pablo bastion
E. Revelin
FGH. Demilunes
K. Powder magazine
L. Storeroom with ship's stores
M. Room with arms
N. Room with provisions
O. Room with arms and military stores
P. Room with provisions
Q. Quarters of the lieutenant governor of the fort
R. Room with provisions
S. Sacristy
T. Chapel
V. Guardroom officers and men
X. Jail
Z. The "necessary"

1. Blacksmith shop
2. Quarters of the overseer
3. Room with provisions
4. Royal Accountant's office
5. Storeroom with artillery stores
6. Calaboose
7. Small closet
8. Room where rations are distributed
9. Storeroom for the *situado* goods from New Spain
10. Powder magazine entrance
11. Storeroom for small stores
12, 13. Ramps
14. Fixed bridge of planks
15. Drawbridge
16, 17, 18, 19. Moat
20. Entrance to the fort
21. Gate
22, 23, 24. Fresh water wells

of the construction crew, who were consulted by the governor. Before the end of this day, Zúñiga and his two royal officials again met in a secret conference to discuss the Camacho mission, which for unrecorded reasons had failed to leave the port. Nothing is known about the deliberation, but apparently Father Camacho was relieved of his task to sail to Havana (*46, 47*).

At eight o'clock on the morning of November 7, the guards at the fort sighted three English sails heading south. Several hours later a messenger arrived from Captain Horruytiner, who was still operating along the mouth of the Salamototo, saying that enemy vessels were heading toward the castle. Since the ships did not stop at St. Augustine, it was believed that they were sailing southward to Matanzas Inlet to block that vital passage, an alternate entrance to St. Augustine harbor. This news disturbed the governor. The royal frigates "La Gloria" and "Nuestra Señora de la Piedad y el Niño Jesús" had been ready to depart for Havana for two months, but had been delayed because of rough weather and contrary winds. "La Gloria" was supposed to have carried Father Camacho. That same day, November 7, the wind and weather were favorable, but due to the English arrival the sailing was suspended. The governor rushed a message to the strong watch station at Matanzas Bar to be on the alert. The post was so located behind the shallow bar that it was safe from a frontal attack by sea or land. Zúñiga reminded the Matanzas garrison to be on guard against any surprise or stratagem (*48*).

Late in the afternoon further news arrived from Horruytiner, saying that he had counted ten small sails, including sloops, brigantines, and a man-of-war (*48*). The governor realized that the English force might be even larger than estimated, and that his task of holding the fort would be difficult. Once more he decided to get in touch, if possible, with Pensacola and Mobile. If the eastern route to Havana was blocked, why not try to reach Cuba via these two western ports? It was the governor's opinion that Father Camacho was not physically able to walk the eighty leagues to Apalachee and then sail to Havana. Consequently, he told his lieutenant governor at San Luis, Manuel Solana, to organize the trip. Solana was to select the captain of the reserve, Jacinto Roque Pérez, and Ensign Diego de Florencia, both stationed in Apalachee, to sail to Pensacola and French Mobile to get "some men, arms, and ammunition." Roque was to continue with the sloop from Pensacola to Havana. Both officers were to leave within a few hours, after having

received their orders from Solana. Zúñiga recommended that Roque go by sea and Florencia by land via Santa Rosa [Island?], and that each carry copies of the other's letters. The governor thought so much of this mission that he decreed negligence on the part of Solana, Roque, or Florencia would be punishable by death. Zúñiga made it clear that Roque himself must go to Havana, but it was not recorded whether Florencia was to go to Mobile in person or whether the Spanish commander at Pensacola would make the contact with the French. The mail messengers, Blas Caballero and Manuel Fernández, carried the orders to Solana (*48, 49, 76*).

At dawn on November 8 Zúñiga inspected the artillery and came to the conclusion that it was deficient. There were too few men and they were not well trained. There were too few guns and what they had were too weak, since the largest gun in the castle was a sixteen-pounder. He told his officers that his gunners "had no service record, lack discipline, and have only a slight knowledge of the bronze and iron guns which are mounted" in the fort (*55*). After studying the records, one cannot but be impressed with the governor's straightforwardness and decisiveness. There was nothing pompous, artificial, or exaggerated in his actions. Although his garrison was short of everything, he was determined to face up to the English the best way he could.

At eight o'clock, just after Zúñiga's artillery inspection, the enemy arrived in full force from the sea. Thirteen ships were sighted from the fort, and at around eleven o'clock it was clear that they were heading toward St. Augustine inlet rather than continuing south as had the three previous ones. By noon Diego de la Sierra, the pilot, who was stationed on the royal frigate "Nuestra Señora de la Piedad y el Niño Jesús" commanded by Luis Alfonso and which lay outside the bar with sixteen men aboard, reported that the English were fast approaching the bar. Immediately the governor ordered Captain Alfonso and Pilot Sierra to board the frigate, bring her over the bar into the harbor, and anchor her alongside the other royal frigate, "La Gloria," under the protection of the fort guns. Both navy men hastened to save their ship from the enemy. Could they do it? (*55, 56, 50*).

While Alfonso and Sierra were rushing to rescue their valuable frigate, Captain Horruytiner returned to the fort at one o'clock with his twenty infantrymen from the mouth of the Salamototo. He had failed in his assigned task to join Fuentes' decimated unit and hold San Juan del Puerto and Piribiriba. Yet Horruytiner did not return empty-handed,

for he brought with him two English prisoners and a Chiluque Indian of the Carolina forces, whose capture he had earlier communicated to Zúñiga. The two Englishmen were immediately submitted to a preliminary examination by Zúñiga, the troop commander Adjutant Bernardo Nieto de Carvajal, and Captain Horruytiner, with the help of William Carr, the English ex-prisoner who had become a valuable citizen of St. Augustine and a highly qualified artilleryman. The Englishmen said that Governor Moore had about one thousand men with him at sea and on land. The Carolina army brought sufficient equipment to besiege the castle. They had shovels, spades, pikes, and other items to build trenches and approach-works. According to the prisoners, Moore had "grenades," but did not bring the feared bombs (large explosive shells). It was their estimate that the English army had provisions for a three-month siege. Zúñiga wanted the two men subjected to a more rigorous interrogation, since it was vital to determine exactly whether the English did or did not have bombs. As interpreters he appointed Carr and Juan Martín, another English ex-prisoner who had joined the garrison and who also was a gunner on Alfonso's frigate. Horruytiner and Captain Juan Bernardo were asked to question the Indian, since both men knew the Guale language. Zúñiga asked that the intelligence be given him quickly, so that he could send it on the frigate to Havana (*54*).

Meanwhile, Alfonso and Sierra were having difficulties with their frigate. The English enemy was fast approaching the bar, and seeing the frigate outside the harbor, they were most determined to capture her. The Spanish crew tried to maneuver over the shallow bar into the inlet, but failed because of contrary winds and low tide. Captain Alfonso and Pilot Sierra decided they urgently needed aid from land to sail the ship over the bar or else to defend her from the enemy. They sent Martín Sánchez, the *guardián* of the fort, to get help and bring back the boatswain, who was still ashore. By four o'clock both men returned to the frigate with orders from Zúñiga to cease any risky maneuvers and to sink the ship after removing all valuable material.

By eight o'clock "Nuestra Señora de la Piedad y el Niño Jesús" had been sunk. Bad weather and the nearness of the enemy had jeopardized the task of saving all valuables. The rigging, sails, and artillery had gone down with the ship; only some slings, hardtack, and flour were salvaged. No men were lost, however, and everyone reached the fort in good condition. As soon as they arrived Zúñiga requested the deposition of some witnesses, in order to certify to the voluntary destruction of the

frigate. Pilot Sierra, Martín Sánchez, the cook Diego Gutiérrez, and sailors Miguel Gómez and Pedro Belén, all rendered identical written declarations. The governor next ordered the sixteen-man crew to join the garrison. Many of them, especially Juan Martín, the master gunner, would be valuable additions to the weak artillery of the castle. Others, inept for this task, would have to join the infantry. All sixteen were ordered to swear loyalty to the defense of the fort. An order was given that the new men should receive their proper daily ration of meat and flour (*50, 51, 52, 53, 55, 56, 57*).

Zúñiga had come to the conclusion that the surviving frigate, "La Gloria," must sail under the command of Captain Alfonso to Havana via Matanzas inlet. He told his staff officers that although he had sent orders to Apalachee to request aid from Pensacola, French Mobile, and Havana, it was conceivable that the mail might never reach these places because "of the dangers of the sea and because the enemy is all around. Zúñiga thought Captain Alfonso should try to leave the next day, November 9, after sundown. But he wanted to discuss the trip of "La Gloria" with his treasurer, auditor, army commandant, and the various infantry captains in a staff meeting to be held at seven o'clock the next morning (*54*).

So came to an end another eventful day. The English arrival by sea had materialized and the Spaniards had to account for their first material casualty. Furthermore, the preliminary interrogation of the two English prisoners had revealed some new information.

Early next morning the three prisoners were re-questioned. The first one to testify was a "Joseph Guellemes," apparently Joseph Williams. He was asked to swear by God and his Protestant Bible to tell the truth and only the truth. The interrogator warned him that perjury would automatically lead to death by a firing squad. Williams said that he was forty-one years old and born in "Olderemes" [Oldham?] belonging to "Seltante" [?] in England. He was married, had children, and lived in South Carolina as a shoemaker. Even though Williams was somewhat reluctant in his testimony he revealed some pertinent information. He said that he had left Charleston "between fifteen and twenty days ago" aboard a small sloop called "Lise," which carried nine men and two boys, had no guns, and was commanded by a "John Nubel" [Nobel]. He and Nobel went ashore near the St. Johns River when their sloop became separated from the main contingent. They had been ordered to sail from Charleston to Port Royal to join seven or eight

other sloops, but rough sea did not permit them to enter the harbor; they sailed alone to Florida, trying to contact their companion ships.

Williams said that Moore had approximately one thousand men on land and sea. James Moore came by sea and had as his aide "a colonel who was an experienced corsair who had commanded the men who had sacked Vera Cruz. He was a great soldier." The land forces, according to Williams, were led by another "corsair from Jamaica." Being further pressed by his interrogators, Williams stated that about five hundred Carolinians sailed in fourteen ships and five hundred men composed the land force. Among the English forces were many Indians and some "Lutheran French" and Negroes who had accompanied their masters. Williams stated that the purpose of the English attack was to "win the Royal Fort and conquer it because it is a good fortification and by conquering it they would be strong and free of the French threat since in Charleston they do not have forts." Carr and Martín were still not satisfied with Williams' answers and were convinced that he had still more information. He was ordered to go into more detail.

The shoemaker admitted he knew more. The English had three brigantines which had four-pounder guns. The ship on which Moore traveled had sixteen guns which were eight- and nine-pounders. Of the sloops only the larger ones had artillery. One had eight guns and another had ten, which were all six-pounders. The navy brought along six heavy iron guns—six-, eight-, and ten-pounders—and gun carriages, round shot, chain shot, and the necessary powder. This equipment was earmarked for the capture of the fort. Fearful about bombs, the Spaniards pressed Williams about this item, but the prisoner insisted that he had never seen bombs nor heard that the English were bringing them. He knew that Moore had ordinary "grenades" or shells, but he had not seen mortars for firing them. Williams also professed ignorance about the training of the gunners.[1]

1. The Spanish word *granada* signifies a round, hollow projectile, filled with gunpowder. A powder fuze, ignited by hand or by the firing of a cannon, caused the projectile to explode at a predetermined time. These explosive missiles were effective against both personnel and structures. Small ones made of glass or iron about three inches in diameter were used as hand grenades. Iron *granadas*, or "shells," from about five and a half to eight inches in diameter were fired from guns, howitzers, and small mortars. "Shell" is a relatively modern term; in 1700 the word "bomb" was commonly used in English to differentiate between the hand grenade and the cannon projectile. However, in Spanish, *bomba* meant the *granada real*, a ten-to-thirteen-inch projectile to be fired from powerful mortars that could deliver a vicious, plunging fire at mile range or more. Small, medium, or large,

In answer to the next question Williams responded that the Carolina men had plenty of provisions to maintain a siege for three months. They had much meat, bread, and flour and it was Williams' opinion that supplies could easily be replenished from Carolina. Carr and Martín wanted to know who was really responsible for planning the attack. The Carolina soldier said that Moore was the sole planner and organizer; the English king had nothing to do with the attack, and it took Moore three months to set up the expedition. Moore had confiscated all the ships which entered Charleston; and most of his men were unpaid, but were promised the spoils of victory.

After this the interrogators, at Governor Zúñiga's request, asked Williams several thoughtful questions. Why did the English want to destroy their friendship with the Spaniards "when the people of Carolina had received so many benefits from the presidio?" Had not the Florida authorities rescued, helped, and conveyed the English castaways personally to Carolina? Not only had they received aid but these people had been saved from the hands of the savage Indians by the arrival of Spanish forces. Zúñiga reminded Williams that just after his inauguration he had sent to Charleston another contingent of Englishmen and Negroes who had run ashore just north of St. Augustine. As another token of friendship, the indignant governor cited a recent cash payment, given to a representative from Carolina as compensation for runaway Negro slaves. (John Archdale in 1707 confirmed that Zúñiga had truly helped the English shipwreck victims and wrote of the "kindness" and "wonderful manner" of Governor Zúñiga [*3*, p. 301].) Shoemaker Williams, utterly confused, responded meekly that he knew all this, but the honorable governor and his interpreters must remember that he was only a simple soldier who had nothing to do with policy matters. After all, he said, the "responsibility of making war on Florida rested with the governor and parliament of [Carolina]." Asked if he knew anything else, the Carolinian said that they might as well kill him because he knew absolutely nothing else. This was accepted as sincere and Zúñiga ordered the man well treated; if he had told the truth he had no reason for fear. Shoemaker Williams was then returned to the fort prison (*60*).

After this William Nobel testified, giving similar answers with minor

---

exploding projectiles lobbed into the mass of humanity crowded into the fort would wreak fearful destruction. Hence the Spanish concern as to the nature of the enemy artillery matériel.

discrepancies and often adding new details. He identified himself as forty-six years old, a businessman born in "Fanton" [Faystown?], New England, married, and a citizen of Charleston. His son, John Nobel, owned the sloop "Lizebela" on which they had come to Florida as part of the Moore expedition. He and his son had come recently from Jamaica. When they had entered Charleston, their sloop was confiscated and they were forced to join Moore's army. Three months ago they had left Charleston with nine men aboard but outside Port Royal lost their anchor. He too said that Moore had about a thousand men, which included "370 Indians, Yamasees, Chiluques, Apalachicolas and other nations, plus some Christian [natives] from these [Spanish] provinces." He said that they had plenty of muskets made in England. The Indians carried guns manufactured in Holland which were of inferior quality; they had a narrower barrel which became hot after eight shots. According to Nobel, a certain Captain James Risbee, who had been in St. Augustine, was the most vociferous proponent in the Assembly of the St. Augustine attack. Risbee had said it would be extremely easy to conquer the presidio and fort, and he had talked Moore into proposing the venture to the legislature.

Nobel claimed that Moore had confiscated forty ships, but used only fourteen plus forty canoes. On the ships he had five hundred men, including some eighty experienced sailors. With him were two excellent commanders who were corsairs, Captain Daniel, a veteran of the "pillage of Vera Cruz," and Captain James Risbee. The attacking army had six heavy iron cannon of different calibers, the largest a twelve-pounder. They had no bombs, because these large explosive shells were not available in Carolina. Nobel was not sure whether they brought mortars for smaller shells. He had seen the English trying to make mortars out of lead, but after three smeltings they were not successful. Even if they tried again after he left, he was doubtful that their gunners had enough experience to fire mortar projectiles.[2] According to Nobel Moore had provisions, especially barrels of salted meat, hardtack, and flour, for a three-month siege, and in all other matters his answers agreed with those of Williams.

2. A properly equipped siege train needed at least two types of cannon: the heavy, low-trajectory guns that fired solid shot to dismount the fort cannon and breach the walls; and the high-trajectory mortars which threw projectiles over and behind the walls to explode among the defenders. As the record shows, the English had only light, low-trajectory pieces. Their heaviest gun fired a twelve-pound shot which had little effect on the thick walls of the fort.

Realizing that Nobel was better educated than his companion and was up to date on current events, the Spaniards decided to ask him about San Jorge (Charleston). Nobel readily supplied the desired information, showing none of Williams' reticence. He said Charleston did not have a fort. The only defense work was "one bastion that has eighteen guns of different calibers." Carolina had no paid soldiers, only militiamen. Continuing his testimony, Nobel stated that the colony had few whites but plenty of slaves. However, two places had many whites. One was identified as Yslandra and had up to twenty houses. The other was in the "neighborhood of *sienmillas* in the inland plantation region and had up to two thousand men." The bar at Charleston harbor had fourteen feet of water at high tide; yet not long ago, Nobel revealed, a forty-gun ship was lost crossing the bar. The talkative businessman stated that Moore "was married and had many children, and sheep and goat and cattle ranches, and plantations, and he has plenty of slaves on his plantation located two days from Carolina [Charleston?], of which he is a veteran settler." Nobel professed to know nothing about Port Royal because he had never been there. Thus terminated the questioning of this prisoner who was then returned to the prison at the fort (*62*).

The Indian was the last to testify. He was not asked to take an oath in the name of God Almighty but he promised to tell the truth to Lorenzo Horruytiner and Juan Bernardo. He said that he was Manuel Agramón; "he was from one of the places of the Chiluques to whose nation he belongs." He had no job and had no idea how old he was, but his interrogators estimated him to be about twenty years old. Agramón stated that he did not know why Williams and Nobel wanted him to go ashore with them at the mouth of the Salamototo. He had come with the English army because he was an experienced sailor, and his masters paid him "ten pesos every month." The Chiluque professed ignorance about the army except to say that they came with iron balls "to kill the Spaniards." He did say that all the other Indians were coming by land and that he knew nothing about them, except that each had a flintlock musket (*escopeta*), a pistol, and a short curved broadsword, called *alfanje*. To all other questions he answered negatively, saying that he did not speak English and therefore was not aware of the doings of the Carolinians. The only important piece of news the Spaniards were able to get from Agramón was a statement that another contingent had left or was to leave from South Carolina to make war on Apalachee (*61*).

While the four men of the intelligence team interrogated the three prisoners, the staff meeting called by the governor for seven o'clock in the morning started punctually, although the various captains were excused because of more urgent work. Treasurer Luis de Florencia and accountant Juan de Pueyo, with the governor presiding, discussed the relief mission to Havana. It was agreed that a man of common sense, initiative, and diplomatic tact should go. All three thought that no officer could be spared in these grave hours since Captain Romo de Urisa with twenty men was already absent in Apalachee. The three men named Sebastián Groso, senior sacristan of the parochial church, for this task. Zúñiga said that Groso had an excellent record, rising from common soldier to adjutant of the reserve and then to sexton, and had shown "enthusiasm on all occasions in which he had served His Majesty." Permission for a leave of absence was at once requested from Ignacio de Leturiondo, vicar and ecclesiastic judge of Florida; it was readily given. Groso was informed of his orders and at ten o'clock embarked in "La Gloria," captained by Luis Alonso. They sailed down the Matanzas River to bypass the blockading boats and slip out by the Matanzas Inlet, under the protection of the watch station six leagues south of the castle. Would the frigate reach Havana and would Groso and Alonso receive aid? If so, would it arrive on time? With "La Gloria" went the hopes of the hard-pressed presidio of St. Augustine (*58*).

As Groso started down-river, three messengers were sent ahead in a fast canoe to Matanzas with the news of "La Gloria's" exit maneuver. The Matanzas garrison was ordered to determine whether there was a reasonably safe passage over the bar, and if English ships were blocking it. The guards were to stop the Spanish frigate to keep her from being intercepted by the enemy. The escape plan of the aid ship was based on the calculation that the English vessels could not come close to the bar because of shallow water, while the Spanish frigate was light and could easily cross it and sail close inshore. By following this procedure, Alonso and Groso did manage to evade the enemy blockade. The same messengers were also to collect all small craft on the river and anchor them under the fort, but they located only one raft. It was across from the Matanzas tower on the west shore of the river, loaded with stone. Since it was too heavy to sail to St. Augustine they sank her (*64*).

Soon after the departure of Groso, two Apalachee Indians arrived

at the fort and said that they had seen and contacted the enemy. They were immediately taken to the governor. The Apalachees failed to identify the exact location of the English army but they said that the enemy was about six or seven leagues from St. Augustine and had "many people" who were rapidly advancing toward St. Augustine by land. Zúñiga estimated that the English land forces might reach the presidio the next day, November 10. At once thirty infantrymen on fast horses left the fort to find the enemy and keep at least one mail route open (*65*).

Zúñiga and his sergeant major, the old Enrique Primo de Rivera, went into conference to debate whether to give battle outside of town or to retreat inside the fort. There was pressure on Zúñiga from some of his captains, and especially from the town's population, to march his men into battlefield and prevent the English occupation of St. Augustine (*66*). Primo de Rivera promised to present to the governor within an hour a complete list of everyone on the garrison payroll. And so he did. His list indicated "three paid companies which amounted to 174 men including the reserve officers and old soldiers." The militia had 44 able men plus some old men and boys of twelve years and more who had never fought. There were 123 Indians from Apalachee, Timucua, and Guale who were experienced with firearms, although their own weapons were useless. There were 57 colored men (free Negroes, mulattoes, and slaves), of which about 20 could handle arms. The four bastions of the fort had 14 artillerymen. The men outside the fort, made up of infantrymen, Indians, Negroes, and mulattoes, "were of little use and service." Primo de Rivera wrote that he could muster altogether 412 men; but of these only 18 infantry soldiers and 18 militiamen were experienced and able to fight an open battle. The best soldiers were in Apalachee, the others were too old or too young, and the Indians and Negroes could not be trusted (*63*).

Studying the sergeant major's memorandum, Governor Zúñiga came to the conclusion that the maximum number of men fit for battle that he could employ in open combat was about seventy. He was sure this was an open invitation to defeat, and would drain his best men away from a successful defense of the castle, which must be kept in Spanish hands at any cost. Therefore it was decided that the garrison and inhabitants must withdraw within the fort and sustain a siege (*66*). Reviewing the situation the executive became aware that not all the people had followed his previous order to go to the castle. He again

called on everyone to obey his instructions forthwith, to pick up their belongings and "carry them in carts, horses, canoes, and on their shoulders" to the fort. By proclamation he informed the people that when they heard three shots and the sound of the main bell of the fort, everyone outside the fort must rush in, because the gates would close soon afterward. No one must fall into the hands of the English, and people were clearly made responsible for avoiding capture (*65, 66*).

Orders were sent to the mounted patrol officers of the various sentinel posts located "outside the fort on the roads and avenues on which . . . the enemy will advance." They were to stay at their posts and inform the fort of the movements of the enemy. The governor reminded the officers of their tremendous responsibility, and that failure to do their utmost duty would seriously handicap the defense. The men were promised that once their reports were no longer needed they would be brought inside the fort (*66*).

All during the afternoon of November 9 the people of St. Augustine and refugees from the countryside poured into the fort. It was a colorful stream of *criollos,* Spaniards, Negroes, mulattoes, and Indians, carrying their meager belongings, some driving their animals into the rapidly decreasing space of the castle. Most spectacular was the sudden arrival of some refugees from San Juan del Puerto "who had left in a violent rush because the enemy had burst in with blood and fire, completely leveling the village." By nightfall the number of refugees had risen so high that Zúñiga called an urgent meeting of his royal officials and the employees of the royal treasury to discuss the problem of the non-garrison element which had gathered within the fort. At eight o'clock sharp the men met in the governor's quarters. Zúñiga said that it was his duty and moral obligation to protect all people of all races who lived under the Spanish flag. It was decided that everyone must be fed, free of charge without any discrimination of rank, age, or race. The supply officer (*escribano de raciones y municiones*) was made responsible for the welfare of the civilians (*59*).

3. THE SIEGE

At dawn on November 10 several Spanish patrols on fast horses left the fort to check on the enemy's advance. They quickly returned as the enemy's land forces, led by Colonel Daniel, overestimated by Zúñiga at one thousand men, soon entered St. Augustine and occupied it without any opposition. They had gone up the St. Johns River in canoes to a point due west of St. Augustine and then marched overland. The heavy gates of the fort closed with 1,500 people inside. Six hundred were fairly able men, although many were unfit for strenuous work. The English commander decided to make his headquarters in the town's largest building, the Franciscan monastery. In a swift move the English infantry advanced along the royal highway toward the mission and village of Nombre de Dios, which had a stone church "a cannon shot" from the castle. At the same time the English navy maneuvered to land men and matériel. Governor Zúñiga said that he counted fourteen English ships, of which seven or eight were sloops, three brigantines, and one frigate, the others not being identified. Little else is told about the actual occupation. The Spaniards, according to Zúñiga's plan, had practically handed over the town, and the Carolinian army simply walked in without opposition (*68, 71, 72, 73, 9*).

As soon as the gates of the fort closed, Zúñiga released an order freeing all the prisoners with the exception of the three men captured from the Moore army. Most of the freed men were Spaniards and *criollos* condemned to hard labor in the presidio, Negroes, mulattoes, and some Indians who were part of the labor gangs for various crimes committed. The governor did not give the number of prisoners but he made it clear that his action must be approved by the home office, since he had requested complete freedom, full pardon, and restoration of their rights. The Florida executive said that his action was a calculated risk. It would be difficult to watch these men during the siege while 1,500 persons plus animals were crowded into the castle. Prisoners could easily escape and desert to the English, providing them with vital information such as the exact strength of the St. Augustine and Apalachee garrison. Zúñiga was fearful that the enemy would learn of Groso's successful evasion of the blockade and dispatch a fast

ship "to Cayo Hueso [Key West] which they called Cuchiaga . . . twenty-five leagues from Havana" to intercept the frigate or disrupt the aid fleet from Cuba. So he gave instructions to watch the prisoners as much as possible. Included in the pardon was the English prisoner Andrew Ransom, who had been captured in 1686 and condemned to death as a pirate but who was granted sanctuary by the Franciscans when the gallows rope broke during the hanging. Sixteen years of legal arguments over Ransom had passed, during which he enjoyed religious asylum; and in the meanwhile he had become an excellent cabinetmaker respected by most St. Augustinians (*68*).

Several more times the fort gates opened that day. Just as the English troops landed, a fast-riding Spanish patrol stampeded 163 head of cattle through the English lines and in a spectacular show drove the animals into the fort moat, accompanied by the cheers of the Spaniards. The governor was delighted by this feat and instructed the reserve adjutant, Joseph Rodríguez Meléndez, to take charge of the cattle. He was instructed that no owner of the animals should suffer any loss and that Rodríguez Meléndez must carefully record the fate of each animal and transcribe the brand mark. This information must then be given to the royal officials, who would reimburse the owners. The arrival of the cattle made the endurance of the siege a better prospect (*71*).

Soon after the cattle arrived, two mail messengers left the besieged fort with letters to Lieutenant Governor Solana of Apalachee, and Lieutenant Governor Diego de Jaen of Timucua, who resided in Santa Fe. Jaen was ordered to take his few soldiers and move to San Luis in Apalachee, because it was expected that the English would likewise attack "the vast province of Apalachee which is eighty leagues from this fort." An Indian uprising in Apalachee was not considered out of the question. Jaen was also told that help for Apalachee from St. Augustine at this time was impossible. A copy of a letter to Solana in San Luis was included in Jaen's letter, while another messenger carried the original to Apalachee. To Solana, Zúñiga outlined the events of the past days. He wrote that he could withstand a long siege, and Solana was ordered to see to it that the Franciscan friars were recalled inside the stockade of San Luis and therefore avoid the spreading of false rumors. After this the captain should call a meeting of the Indian chiefs without interference from the friars, and assure the natives that the Spanish would smash the English attack. He was

THE ART OF WAR AT THE BEGINNING OF THE 1700's

(From Volume III of A. M. Mallet's *Le Travaux de Mars, ou l'Art de la Guerre* published at Amsterdam in 1696, pp. 33, 47, 159, 243.)

(33) The matchlock musket pictured here was .70 caliber and had a 45-inch barrel. Its range was about 250 yards. Along with the lighter arquebus and the dependable old pike (note the pikeman at left), it was a standard infantry weapon in 1702. The flintlock musket was not yet in general use.

OU L'ART DE LA GUERRE. 47

OU L'ART DE LA GUERRE. 159

OU L'ART DE LA GUERRE. 243

reminded to keep in contact by duplicate mail with Pensacola and Mobile, and he must encourage the French commander's intention to march on Charleston. Solana was informed that Groso had successfully departed for Havana and carried with him "powers and letters for the French fleet which is over there." It is assumed from this statement that the French fleet was in Havana and that the Carolinian fear of an allied attack was well founded (*72, 73*).

The lieutenant governor at Apalachee was asked also to maintain communications with the fort and to send continuous mail, and Governor Zúñiga promised to do the same. He was sure that the messengers with their expert knowledge of the country could easily make it through the English lines. The most pertinent news should be handled vocally and not by letters or memorandums. Each mail carrier should carry two letters, a short one summarizing the pertinent information in such a fashion that if the enemy got hold of it he could not understand it, and the second one, more detailed, should be a false one which if it fell into the enemy's hands must "inspire terror and discourage him, thereby causing him to lift the siege." A copy of the vocal information must be filed with the royal scrivener so that a thorough record could be kept. It is not recorded if this system was successful or was followed, but communication with the west was maintained, and the English were unable to stop the passage of messengers who diligently crossed swamps and palmetto thickets to reach the fort (*72*).

By midday on November 10 the English were continuing their landings. The Spaniards soon began to open fire whenever the English came within range of their guns, but without any hits. The artillerymen were out of practice; this was their first active battle duty for a long

AT LEFT:

(47) Here is the musketeer in action: A—with match burning, ready for a command; B—at ease; C—waiting for the order to fire; D—aiming; and E—aiming from the kneeling position. Musketeers probably comprised 25 per cent of the Spanish infantry at St. Augustine. The other foot soldiers were arquebusiers (about 37 per cent) and pikemen.

(159) This picture of mortars lobbing "bombs" explains the Spanish relief at learning that their attackers had no such weapons. Mortars ranged about a mile, and walls were no protection against their plunging fire. Note that the center soldier is using a gunner's quadrant to set elevation. At left the intrepid mortarman has just ignited the bomb fuze by means of the matchcord in his right hand; he will next fire the mortar with the matchcord in his *left* hand.

(243) Siege trenches, called "saps," enabled attackers to approach a fort in comparative safety. Notice the gabions (bottomless baskets) under construction in the foreground. Set along a shallow trench and filled with earth, they made a musketproof wall. Gabions and trenches had a prominent part in the siege at St. Augustine.

time. The western bastions of the fort concentrated fire on the Carolinians "who were passing along the *playazco* [large beach] close to the shores of the [San Sebastián] river two musket shots away from the fort." The fire was continuous and the men enthusiastic; then suddenly the sixteen-pounder iron gun in San Pablo bastion exploded with a terrific roar, instantly killing Juan de Galdona, the gunner in charge of the bastion. Another artilleryman and a militiaman were so severely hurt that they died within a few minutes. Five other men were carried away seriously injured by the splinters, but these men recovered. Zúñiga, who had rushed to the scene of the accident, ordered everyone away from the bastion and asked the other gunners to cease firing. He ordered the artillery officers to meet with him immediately.

It was determined on the spot that the old gun had been overloaded with round shot, bar shot, and grapeshot, besides being slightly cracked. The governor blamed the artillerymen for this disaster, since they had failed to check the gun and had not detected the crack. Zúñiga did not absolve the crown, which was indirectly to blame because it had failed to send new guns which had been asked for continuously. The ones on hand were light iron and so old that they could no longer be used for their prescribed caliber. Zúñiga told Sergeant Major Primo de Rivera to check all the iron and bronze guns and determine the amount of powder that could be used safely for "the first, second, and third [proof] charges." The commander was advised to get the expert help of Juan Martín, master gunner of the sunken frigate, and Alonso García, master gunner of the fort. When these two men finished, the governor personally inspected the guns and had each one fired in his own presence (*70*). After this, Zúñiga decided that the army commander Primo de Rivera, who suffered from old age, should be partly relieved, and he named Adjutant Bernardo Nieto de Carvajal as commander of orders and chief aide-de-camp. Primo de Rivera would keep the honor of the title and would be respectfully consulted (*74*).

On the morning of November 11 Governor Zúñiga gave his officers a quick review of the military situation in accordance with the reports of the patrols. The English land force had taken all of the town and established its headquarters in the friary of St. Francis "one cannon shot from this royal fort." The English ships had crossed the bar and were still landing their men, but apparently had not yet crossed the bay and joined up with the land forces. Till they did so was only a question of time because the guns of the fort could not stop them. The

greatest obstacles for effective bombardment of the English forces were the many houses standing near the fort. Furthermore, the English could occupy these houses, emplace their guns, and do serious damage to the fort. So out of the war council came orders to organize "a sally of brave men escorted by two lines of musketeers in order to put to the torch all the large and small houses." This tactic would make sure that the English forces could not "set their batteries against this royal fort at their pleasure." Bernardo Nieto de Carvajal was to contact all owners of the condemned houses and give them permission to leave the fort at their own risk and rescue any possession. Zúñiga wanted the fire patrol to burn the houses early the next morning. (But probably this order was not carried out until November 14 [*74*].)

The next two days are not well accounted for in the documentary annals of history. Apparently the military situation was calm. The Spaniards remained inside the castle knowing that they could not stop the besieging maneuvers. The English began to establish positions, aware that only a long siege could lead to victory. In the interior the situation was confusing. Guale was lost and the Spanish troops were captured or were astray in the swamps. On November 13 the lieutenant governor of Timucua, Diego de Jaen, had led his soldiers from Santa Fe to San Francisco when he received Zúñiga's order to move to San Luis in Apalachee. Jaen called the Indian chiefs into council and then left for Apalachee. He sent word that the natives were calm and apparently no incident occurred in Timucua during the Moore siege (*77*). News from Apalachee was more obscure. Lieutenant Governor Solana stated on November 13 that he had already received three letters from Zúñiga and had obeyed the various orders the best he could. Solana called in the Indian chiefs and discussed the local and international situation with them. He was satisfied as to their apparent loyalty. Solana had some minor problems, however, about sending messengers to Pensacola and Mobile. Captain Roque was very anxious to go and the captain and crew of the Havana ship did not object to the governor's orders, although they did ask to be furnished provisions for such a journey. It was learned later that the ship leaked badly and had to be put in drydock, which prevented an immediate departure. Part of the Apalachee garrison at San Luis was ordered to St. Marks to speed up the repair. While the work progressed the latest order from Zúñiga arrived, to dispatch Roque to Havana via Pensacola. Ensign Florencia was to go with him to Pensacola, in order to get in contact with Mobile.

When Zúñiga's order arrived, Solana ordered a staff meeting at St. Marks at midnight, November 11. The ship's captain was in Ayubale, apparently in search for repair material, and Florencia was also out of town. But both came by fast horses through the dark night to St. Marks, as did Roque and Solana. When they inspected the ship they decided she was not yet ready to go; but as if Heaven intervened, a ship from St. Joseph's Bay arrived the same night. Next morning, November 12, Ensign Florencia departed on the St. Joseph's ship to Pensacola, carrying the letters for this Spanish outpost and for the French in neighboring Mobile. Roque remained in St. Marks until the Havana ship was repaired, and sailed on her to Cuba on an undetermined date the same month (*76*, *90*, *96*).

Back in St. Augustine, the English occupied the village of Nombre de Dios, a half mile north of the fort, early on November 14. The guards from the fort bastions saw the English banner flying "from the stone church" at Nombre de Dios. Zúñiga was not pleased with this development because, as he said, the Carolinians could now "cover the paths and roads which our people must take in order to get to it [Nombre de Dios?], and those who come from Timucua and Apalachee as well as those who come from other places and ranches in the northern area." It meant, according to the governor, that the English could use the thickets along the road to ambush the men who left the walls to cut forage for the cattle in the moat.

On the same day it was confirmed that the English had occupied the house of Adjutant Joseph Rodríguez Meléndez, which was located exactly southwest of the main gate of the fort. The Rodríguez house was identified as being "the strongest, newest, and highest which had remained standing [and] . . . from its balconies can be seen those who enter and leave this fort." Therefore whoever occupied this house could command the ravelin which protected the fort gate. The English had moved some of their light guns to this house. In view of this situation, Zúñiga ordered the chief aide-de-camp, Nieto de Carvajal, to consult with the sergeant major in organizing another sally to destroy the thickets along the Nombre de Dios road and burn the adjutant's house and others nearby. The Spanish sallies destroyed a great part of St. Augustine located in the neighborhood of the fort (*78*). But even though the houses were destroyed Zúñiga still worried about his weak ravelin, because the Moore forces could build a high earthwork from which to shoot into the gate. An order was given to Adjutant Fabián de

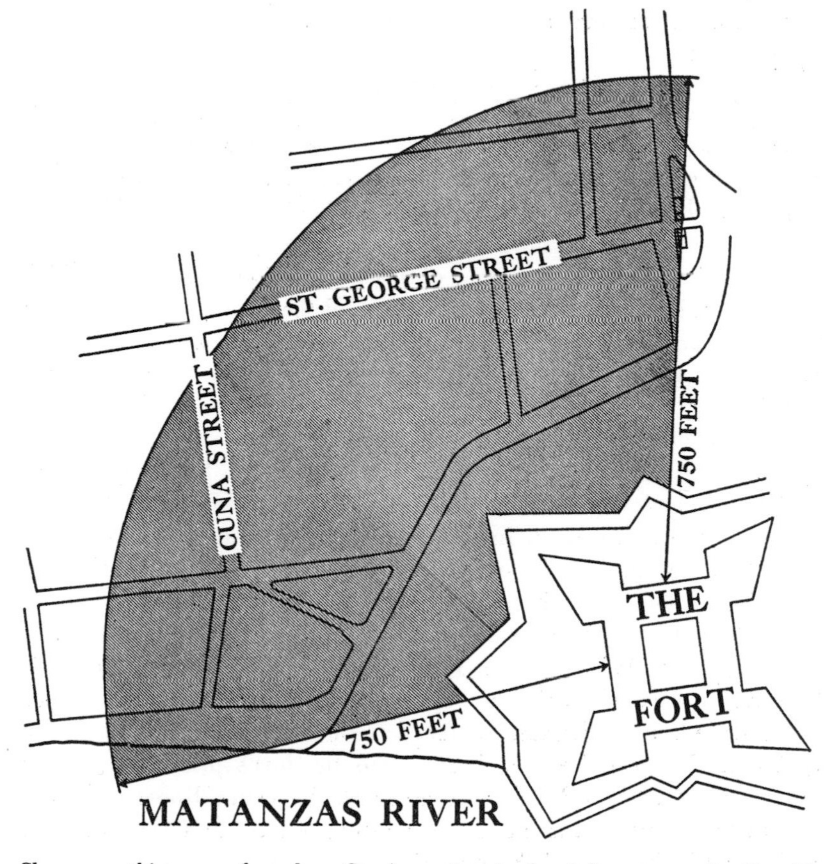

Shown on this map of modern St. Augustine is the defense zone the Spanish cleared by destroying their houses within "a musket shot" of the fort (*74*).

Angulo, who was the foreman of the royal shops, to build a high and strong palisade to protect the gate (*79*).

The wheels of Spanish bureaucracy turned slowly. The governmental appraisal of the burned houses was not made until August, 1709, under the governorship of Francisco de Córcoles y Martínez, although a royal cédula of July 22, 1703, had requested it. On January 9, 1708, Córcoles appointed Captain Francisco Romo de Uriza, commander of the infantry, and Adjutant Rodríguez Meléndez as representatives of the crown, and Captain Joachim de Florencia and Manuel Gonzales Ventura as representatives of the owners, to appraise the value of the burned property. The final report showed that the Spanish sallies had destroyed the property of thirty-one people, valued at 15,430 pesos. The house

of Captain Joseph de León had the highest value, appraised at 6,000 pesos. Three houses were valued at only 50 pesos each because they were made of "straw and boards." Two other houses were listed at 60 and 70 pesos each. The average house was valued from 200 to 500 pesos. The house of the colorful English citizen, Guillermo Carr, was burned by the Spanish sally and was valued at 500 pesos because it was "all of wood." The residence of Joseph Rodríguez Meléndez, which the English had used to fire on the gate and the ravelin, was appraised at 1,200 pesos. Therefore the burning of St. Augustine of 1702 was not exclusively an English task, for the responsibility lay also with the Spaniards (*142*).

By November 16 the English were still trying to consolidate their positions, forming a narrower circle around the fort. Spanish artillery was active and kept the Moore troops away from the immediate neighborhood of the moat. In some undetermined way a path was kept open to the west, because on the morning of November 16 Captain Francisco Romo de Uriza of the infantry arrived at the fort from Apalachee with two soldiers and a militiaman. With them they brought in shackles an Indian called Jalaph Baltasar from San Martín de Thomale in Apalachee. He was captured on November 15 on the king's road, travelling in disguise to the fort, and paid by the English to gather intelligence. He was thrown into the fort's prison. When the contingent had reached the environs of St. Augustine Romo de Uriza, known for his valor and daring, had ventured into the downtown area and found it lifeless and the English army quiet.

The next week of the siege was evidently uneventful; the records give little or no detail. On November 22 Zúñiga reported that the enemy had "taken possession of this town and its neighborhoods" but had done nothing to storm the fort, nor was he building trenches and approachworks; neither was it apparent that he was going to do so. The Moore army was intermittently shooting at the castle with nine- to twelve-pounder guns that were completely ineffective against the thick walls. By now Zúñiga knew that Governor Moore had dispatched Colonel Daniel to Jamaica for "men, bombs, and bigger guns."

The Spanish governor lacked detailed information, however, so he gave a secret order for a Spanish patrol of fifteen or sixteen infantrymen on fast horses to leave the fort during the night and try to capture enemy soldiers who traveled the road from Nombre de Dios to the Franciscan monastery (*80*).

During the night of November 22 the patrol ambushed four men who were riding from Nombre de Dios. In the skirmish, two Englishmen escaped on their horses after being slightly wounded. A Thomas Jones surrendered immediately; John Day was captured when galloping away, after taking blows from a Spanish lance on his face and shoulder blade. Both men were rushed to the fort where Day received medical attention. It turned out that one of them carried a letter from the English commander of Nombre de Dios, identified as John Martin, to Governor Moore. Zúñiga ordered Ransom to translate the letter. After this the prisoners were to be questioned by the same team which interrogated the other captives (*82*, *84*). When the letter was shown to Ransom he said it was hard to read, and asked for the help of William Carr and Bernard Patrick, another English ex-prisoner turned St. Augustinian. All three failed to decipher the text, since they had forgotten much of English writing. Thomas Jones, the recently captured soldier, volunteered to finish the task since he knew Spanish (*85*).

In the letter, Martin, the English commander, complained to Moore that he had not received the field glass which he would need for two or three hours and then return. He was also short of ammunition and his soldiers' bags were empty. He wanted shovels, iron ones if possible, in order to make trenches "to keep the Spaniards from entering the marsh in search of grass for their cattle." Mortars were also needed, for effective bombardment "because the Spaniards are cutting much grass and therefore must have many cattle in the moat of the fort." Martin told Moore that the English must stop this grass-cutting; he said "their ship ought to sail farther up, and then with her canoe possibly catch those who cut the hay." It could not be done from their position at Nombre de Dios because the creek was "too narrow and crooked" and the canoes were "too small and leak very badly." Moreover, wrote Martin, "the machetes which Your Honor had sent us appear to be useless and do not cut because they are dull." He wanted the large box of tools from the flagship "Susan," which the authorities of the ship had refused to hand over. Martin talked about the large sailing vessel "Colami" [?] and said that Captain Risbee was still outside the bar not yet out of sight. In conclusion, Commander Martin wished Governor Moore a pleasant and final victory over the Spaniards (*75*).

The Spanish governor was extremely pleased with the intercepted letter. But he was confused about the "Colami" and the role of Captain

Risbee, so he ordered the two prisoners questioned about it. Jones was the first to testify, after taking an oath "before their God and law" witnessed by the powerful royal scribe, Juan Solana. He was thirty-six years old, a carpenter born in Ostardan [?], England, of Catholic faith but later converted to Protestantism. He said that Moore had one thousand men to take St. Augustine so the French "would not settle it." He cited the equipment of the English already known to the Spaniards from previous declarations, and added fifteen ladders twenty-five feet high and two or four feet wide. Most of the material was still in the ships, but the artillery was on land. The English had one hundred men in Nombre de Dios and had not dug trenches but had eight guard posts one hundred feet from the church. The English had come with thirteen ships to St. Augustine, including the one on which Moore had traveled, which had sixteen guns. One ship was lost when entering the bay, three had returned to Carolina, and two had sailed for Providence in the Bahamas. Jones stated that he knew nothing of the two ships mentioned in the letter, but was informed that a man named Llemes, which most likely was Daniel, was sailing to Jamaica to procure bombs (*83*).

John Day's declaration was much shorter, since the man was still weak from his wounds. He was thirty-two years old, from New England, married, and a sailor. Day said that Moore was living in the Franciscan friary and had sent to Jamaica for bombs. The English governor had told his troops that once the bombs arrived he would conquer the fort. He needed bombs because "this fort was very strong." He had promised his men that he would not "leave this city even if he lost his head." According to this wounded soldier, the English had two companies in Nombre de Dios; some patrols had left to capture cattle, mail, and Indians but had returned empty-handed. He believed that the artillery had been landed and positioned and the English were finishing the siege trenches in St. Augustine. He also spoke of "Llemes." It remains unknown why Risbee's name appears in the captured letter as sailing to Jamaica, when the South Carolina history books state that Daniel went for the bombs, as was confirmed by the two prisoners (*82*).

The news given by Jones and Day about the artillery in position was confirmed on November 24 when the English stepped up the fire on the fort. They had moved four of their heaviest guns into the back yard of the house of Juan de Pueyo, the accountant. This house, according to the Spaniards, was located a musket shot from the castle.

Using these guns the English opened fire with round shot and bar shot. The Spaniards returned the fire from the San Agustín and San Pedro bastions with eighty shots of sixteen- and eighteen-pound cannonballs during twenty-four hours, directing some of their shots against the ships in the harbor. The north bastions, called San Pablo and San Carlos, went into moderate action, shooting at Nombre de Dios.

The English replied, but finding some of the buildings in the way, they set the torch to them. Early on November 25 they began "setting fire to the southern part of the town and the houses immediately next to the Church of Our Lord, St. Francis. They also set fire to the monastery, keeping intact the aforementioned Church." Apparently Governor Moore had his headquarters and living space inside the church. The Spaniards considered it a serious insult and violation of a gentleman's principles *(86)*.

After this skirmish the situation again calmed down. The English were digging siege trenches and waiting for the bombs from Jamaica; the Spanish inside the fort were hoping and praying that a relief force would come from Havana or the west. Groso had made it to Havana, and the governor of Cuba, Pedro Nicolás Benítez de Lugo, had decided on December 2 in war council "to aid this presidio [St. Augustine] with provisions, ammunition, and infantry of this fort" of Havana. The Cuban executive appointed Captain López de Solloso as the infantry relief commander "because he has my full confidence, is honorable and conscientious in his tasks." López de Solloso was a veteran of European wars, but had never been in Florida. His orders were to bring the forces to St. Augustine by way of the St. Augustine entrance, the Matanzas Bar, or the *entrecasco* (a narrow but deep channel at the tip of Vilano Beach) and if this were not possible, to sail up the St. Johns River. In relieving the fort, utmost care must be used and no unnecessary risk was permissible. Once contact was established with the St. Augustine garrison, Captain López de Solloso must put himself under the command of Zúñiga "until his return to this place [Havana] which will be whenever the operations are finished and the siege has been lifted." These last words were underlined and at the margin there was printed in large letters the word *ojo* (take note!) *(91)*.

The same day that the governor of Cuba started to relieve the besieged fort, Ensign Diego de Florencia arrived in Pensacola and went on to Mobile. His journey to Pensacola had taken ten days because "the winds were so contrary." The acting governor at Santa María de

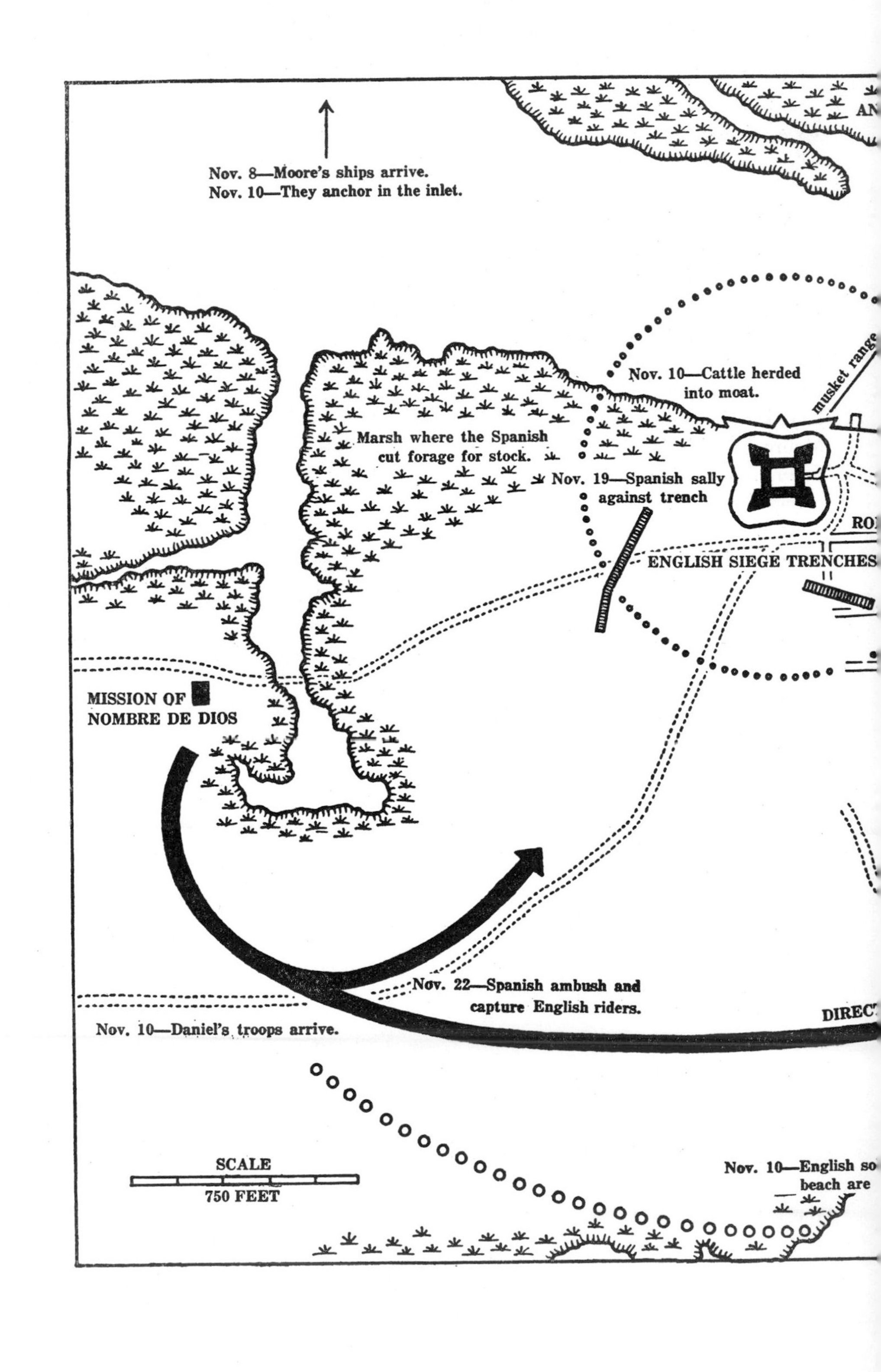
Nov. 8—Moore's ships arrive.
Nov. 10—They anchor in the inlet.
Nov. 10—Cattle herded into moat.
musket range
Marsh where the Spanish cut forage for stock.
Nov. 19—Spanish sally against trench
ENGLISH SIEGE TRENCHES
MISSION OF NOMBRE DE DIOS
Nov. 22—Spanish ambush and capture English riders.
Nov. 10—Daniel's troops arrive.
SCALE
750 FEET

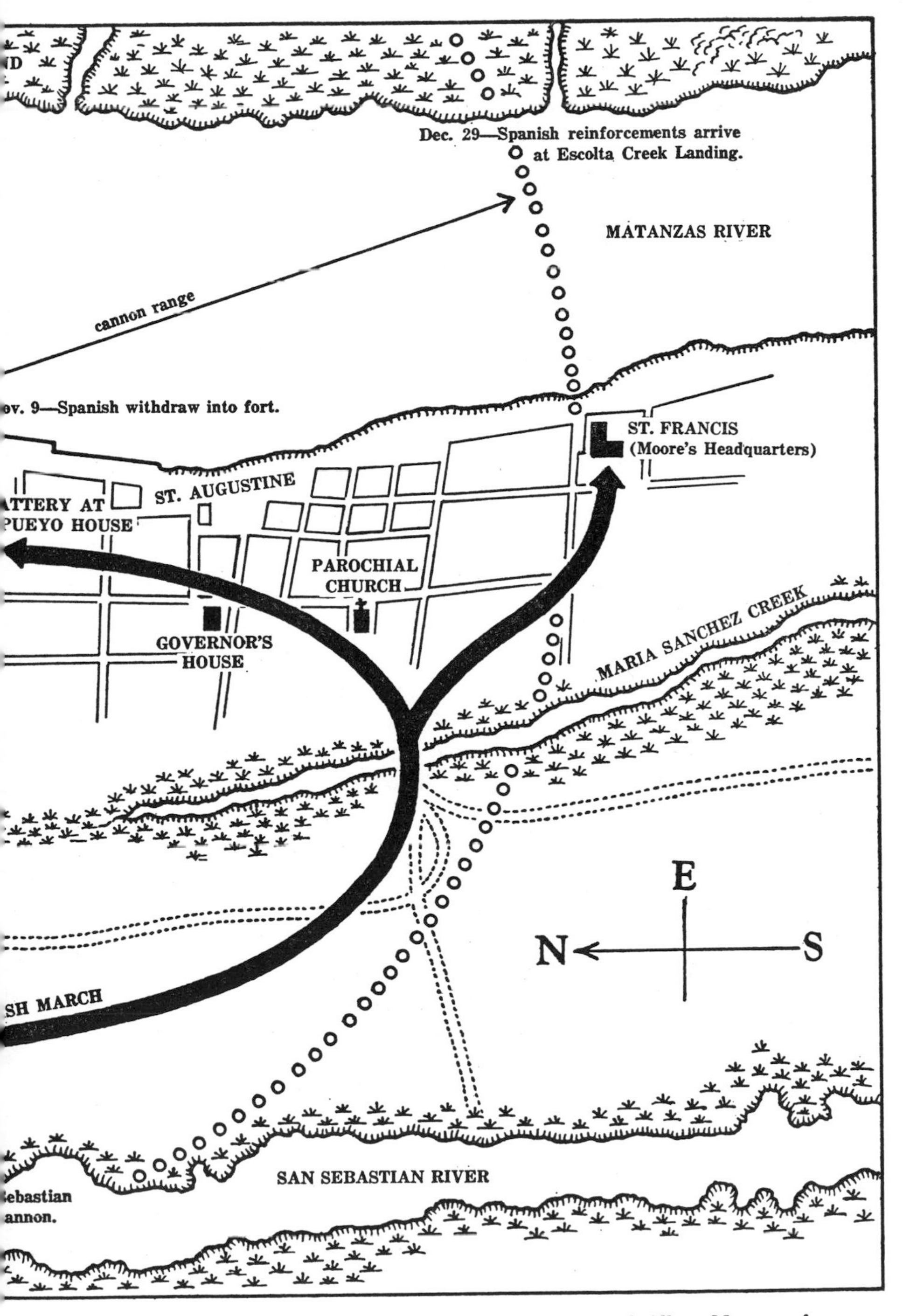

This diagram was prepared by Historians Luis R. Arana and Albert Manucy of the National Park Service staff at Castillo de San Marcos, from the Spanish descriptions of the siege. The topography is from the Arredondo "Plan de la Ciudad de San Agustín" of 1737 (AI 87-1-2/2).

Galve (Pensacola), Francisco Martínez, gave him only ten men, commanded by Ensign Francisco Montes. The French commander of Mobile, Monsieur Berbila, was somewhat more generous. He could not spare men "because he said he had very few and many ill, and he has the work of the fort on his hands." But he gave the Spanish ensign one hundred brand new flintlocks valued at ten pesos each, one thousand pounds of excellent gunpowder costing five hundred pesos, one thousand flints worth eight *reales* each, and two hundred cartridge belts of undetermined value. Florencia got back to San Luis on December 19, and he and Solana left Apalachee for St. Augustine on December 24 with the Pensacola reinforcements. By the time they reached Santa Fe the siege had ended and Zúñiga ordered their return (*89, 96, 130, 9*). But what had happened to Captain Jacinto Roque? Apparently he never reached Havana. On May 24, 1703, long after the siege had terminated, he returned to San Luis, saying that he had gone to Pensacola and Mobile, where he had picked up fifty muskets and five hundred flints at a cost of 503 pesos and six reales. He had received a promise from M. Berbila to help in harassing the English and their Indian allies. Furthermore he sent Zúñiga a description of Mobile. Roque had also sent a message to New Spain from Pensacola, but nothing more is known about his long journey (*139*).

In the meantime, the Spaniards inside the fort had no idea that help was coming, and they settled into a tense routine. Although extremely crowded, the Spanish forces had good morale, while the Carolinians were dissatisfied with Moore, who had promised them an easy victory. On November 24 a small launch with Francisco Domínguez and Lorenzo Ruiz broke the English blockade and sailed for Apalachee with mail, since Zúñiga had not heard from San Luis and thought that the king's road was in the hands of the English forces (*88*). The same day news arrived from the defeated commander of Guale telling of his rout into the swamps. Juan de Orta, the messenger, had defied the English, nature, and Indians in carrying the letter to the fort. He finally made it after many tries, with the help of two loyal Indians. Zúñiga immediately appointed Matheo Suárez, an "expert of these places," and some Indians to carry ammunition to Captain Fuentes in Guale, and told the captain to open guerrilla warfare and raid the English anchorage at the entrance of the Salamototo. Fuentes was also instructed to send the Indian scouts to Santa Fe in Timucua and San Luis in Apalachee to ask for help (*88*).

As can be seen, Zúñiga used every imaginable chance to send mail to the various posts asking for aid. Finally on December 2, the mail carriers Nicolás Monzón and Blas Cavallero arrived at the fort from Timucua and Apalachee, bringing letters from Jaen and Solana. Zúñiga and his staff felt relieved, as it meant that the king's road to the west was at least partially open (*90*). There were some interruptions at the ferry west of St. Augustine. Both messengers had reported that Captain Juan Asemsio, who was in charge of the ferry over the Salamototo, "was forced to retreat from the upper river with the canoes and with all the inhabitants of the village to look for safety." Officer Juan Clemente Horruytiner and Domingo Luján, who were "experts of this river and its neighborhoods," were sent to the Salamototo to "look along the shores for canoes from the little cattle ranches and *haciendas* that are located on the river." They found some peons on the empty ranches who collected five canoes that were taken to the crossing place. Here a messenger was waiting with a letter to Zúñiga from the Indian *cacique* of Timucua, Francisco Rico, stating that Jaen had left Santa Fe for Apalachee. The Spanish messenger Francisco de Castañeda was the first to cross the wide river on December 6 and galloped off for San Luis in the company of some cattle ranch peons. He carried another letter to Solana, requesting help "in case the reinforcements from Pensacola and Mobile have not arrived, of up to six hundred men including Apalachees, Chacatos, and Timucuans plus the soldiers you can spare from the blockhouse." Solana was to leave ten soldiers in San Luis to protect the province with the help of the Indians (*90, 92, 93*).

The apparent calm at St. Augustine was interrupted on December 14 by a minor accident. At seven in the morning the Yamasee Indian Juan Lorenzo, his wife carrying a baby, and a small girl entered the fort and asked for asylum. Lorenzo had a rifle with ample ammunition, something rare for an Indian. He explained that the English had given it to him, but he had escaped and was volunteering information. He said the English had captured the messengers Francisco Domínguez and Lorenzo Ruiz on the way from Apalachee. The captured letter stated that help was coming from the west; therefore Moore had decided to retreat "and burn the houses and the monastery of San Francisco." Zúñiga and his staff were somewhat wary of Lorenzo but gave him freedom. Lorenzo then quietly contacted the Yamasee, Guale, and Apalachee Indians in the fort and proposed that they rebel and capture the fort from the inside. Loyal Indians rushed the news to Zúñiga, who

ordered the detention of Lorenzo and his wife. He was tortured for information but showed great courage and remained silent. His wife and daughter weakened and admitted they had come to blow up the powder house. Lorenzo was identified as an Indian with white blood, a *ladino* who had previously lived in St. Augustine and who had been to jail twice and had escaped. He was then recaptured and sent to jail in Havana from which he also had escaped and joined the English. Zúñiga ordered him put in "a pair of shackles" (*94*).

By December 19 the situation of the besieged fort had deteriorated. The governor reported that the English had dug trenches and other approachworks where they had moved their artillery. Along the trenches they had put up gabions [supports for the earthwork]. These ran from the south to the north-northeast. Another row of gabions ran to the west on the land side, and a third row of sixty-three gabions showed up on December 19, running from the northwest to the east. To the Spaniards this last row, located only a carbine shot from the fort, was the most dangerous since it disrupted their grass cutting for the cattle and horses in the moat. Fray Martín de Alacano tells us that behind the gabions the English had made "dugout caves [bombproofs] in the earth, where they had cover and stayed in complete security" (*141*, fol. 5072). At midday a Spanish sally of fifty-eight men left the fort to smash this nearest row of gabions. The battle was indecisive. The Spanish destroyed part of the gabions and forced the English to retreat, capturing some shovels and bottles of liquor which helped the English "to stand the rigor of the weather and continous cold." The English then reorganized for a counterattack. With help from Nombre de Dios they routed the Spanish, who fled into the fort leaving one dead and carrying several wounded. By the end of the day the English had advanced to within a pistol shot of the fort, where they began to construct new gabions. In view of the gravity of the situation the Spanish authorities ordered ten infantrymen led by two corporals on fast horses to leave during the night for Apalachee to get immediate help. Records do not say if the men were successful in reaching San Luis (*95*).

4. THE ENGLISH WITHDRAWAL

During the next days the front again quieted down, each side still waiting for reinforcements. Inside the fort, morale was beginning to break and tenseness and irritation became noticeable. On December 24 the guard in the lookout noticed two ships on the horizon and sounded an alarm. A tremendous feeling of suspense ran through the fort. Was it the English reinforcements with the bombs from Jamaica or was it help from Havana? A decision was near at hand. By noon disappointment was on everyone's face. The ships were English. It shook the determination of the troops and, according to the governor, brought consternation to the women crowded in the fort. Hoping to alleviate the suffering, the governor ordered a Christmas Eve party organized, in which harps and *vihuelas* should be played "as has been done other nights." Furthermore Zúñiga told the treasurer and the accountant to distribute a Christmas bonus to the troops. When the two men protested that the garrison could not afford it, Zúñiga told them to charge it to next year's account. He said that the troops and people must be cheered up to stop their "melancholic deliberations." Governor Zúñiga was still determined to win this battle and he never wavered in his optimism (*98*).

On Christmas Day the two ships, a brigantine and a sloop, entered the harbor. Zúñiga reported that they brought reinforcements and ammunition which were disembarked on Anastasia Island. Available English records do not mention the arrival of these ships and it is quite certain that they did not come from Jamaica with the dreaded bombs. But this was not known inside the fort, and through the tense populace of the fort rumors spread that bombs had arrived. The governor was worried that panic might break out, so he issued an order forbidding any discussion of the military situation and proclaiming heavy penalties for those who disobeyed. The military commanders were told to continue the same tactics, to keep a twenty-four-hour vigilance on the fort walls and bastions, and the artillery was to maintain its night fire on the enemy's approachworks and trenches. He told the people that up to this day the enemy had not been able to "damage the fort with their grenades and artillery" and he expected the final victory to belong to the Spanish (*99*).

Even so, the morale of the people did not take a swing upward; the whispers in the dark corners of the crowded fort continued. Then suddenly on December 26, around two or three o'clock in the afternoon, sparks of hope illuminated the whole fort. The lookout had seen "four sails" belonging to four powerful men-of-war that certainly resembled the Spanish type. (English sources mention only two vessels.) Zúñiga immediately addressed the people and said that this might be the help he had asked "from here and from Apalachee to Pensacola and Mobile, asking them to transmit it to New Spain and Havana." Or possibly it was the direct result of the Groso mission (*100, 114*). Indeed, it was the relief fleet from Havana! Seeing the four men-of-war, Zúñiga ordered complete silence in the fort so that the guards could "see and listen to the ship movements and signals," for he had instructed Groso to use certain signals upon his successful return. The guards were also instructed to keep a close watch on the enemy, especially along the *Tholomato* and *Punta del Quartel* sectors, and report any move of theirs in view of the new situation. From these two positions athwart the inlet the English could do the most damage to the approaching relief fleet (*100*).

December 27 and 28 were hectic days. It had been definitely established that the ships were Spanish, and this brought a wave of optimism and sheer relief to the frightened people and the tired garrison. More exciting was the report that the eight enemy ships had begun to turn their prows and were lining up with the apparent purpose of leaving the inlet to avoid a trap. Zúñiga hastily summoned a meeting of his naval experts, who came to the conclusion that the English blockade force, because of the dark night and favorable wind, could succeed in its maneuver unless the relief fleet took an aggressive attitude, ready to fight a full-fledged naval battle at the bar. Such a clash was improbable. The Spanish fleet had shown no signs of doing anything, not disembarking the infantry or even getting in touch with the governor, who was incensed by this inaction. He criticized the relief fleet for its lethargy and what he classified as discourtesies. According to the governor, the least its commander could have done was to send a launch through the *entrecasco,* a small channel at the north end of the bar, "rounding the point of present Vilano Beach," then called San Matheo (*15,* p. 32), and anchor off the demilune to establish contact between the fort and the fleet. Zúñiga chose Adjutant Sebastián López de Toledo to slip through the *entrecasco* immediately

and reach the Spanish fleet commander. Toledo took with him a request to land five hundred men and block the exit of the English ships, thereby converting the English blockade into a great Spanish victory (*101*).

December 28 and 29 brought the climax of the long siege. Adjutant López de Toledo, leaving the fort at three o'clock in the morning of December 28, passed expertly through the *entrecasco* and at nine o'clock reached the commandship, the "Black Eagle," anchored three leagues south of the bar and commanded by General Estevan de Berroa. The general assumed a haughty attitude from the very beginning. He had just given orders to swing around and return to Havana because he had failed to receive news from the fort and had assumed that it had fallen into English hands. The governor of Havana later said that General Berroa had signaled four times but failed to get a response from the fort, a statement which Zúñiga contradicted. Captain Joseph Primo de Rivera of the relief infantry admitted that Berroa, under pressure from his sailors, refused to give battle to the cornered English ships, and sailed south to a safe position (*102, 112, 113, 114, 137*, fols. 10434-10432).

In view of the adjutant's arrival, General Berroa decided to remain. By the afternoon of December 29, 212 infantrymen under Captain López de Solloso, which included seventy young Galician recruits destined for the garrison, disembarked on Anastasia Island at a place identified by Diego Caro as "*playa de Mattanzas* [Matanzas beach] at the exact spot called *Mosquitos*," and said by Francisco Basurtto to be three or four leagues from the bar. They reached the Escolta Creek landing (about three miles southeast of St. Augustine) at sunset, intending to cross the Matanzas River to the mainland the next day. Adjutant López de Toledo thought that the initial delay of over a day in debarking the troops and the stop at the Escolta landing facilitated Moore's retreat and lost them a chance to destroy the English. He said flatly that the relief troops refused to go into battle. Later Governor Zúñiga, incensed with Berroa's attitude, classified the 212 men as "most useless." The seventy Galacian recruits he described as "extremely young, some sick and all of them without experience and the military training necessary to handle weapons" (*102, 110, 111, 113, 114, 115, 9*).

On the night of January 29 and early during the next morning the English began their retreat. They hoped to leave by sea and embarked most of their men and equipment in their eight ships, but in the mean-

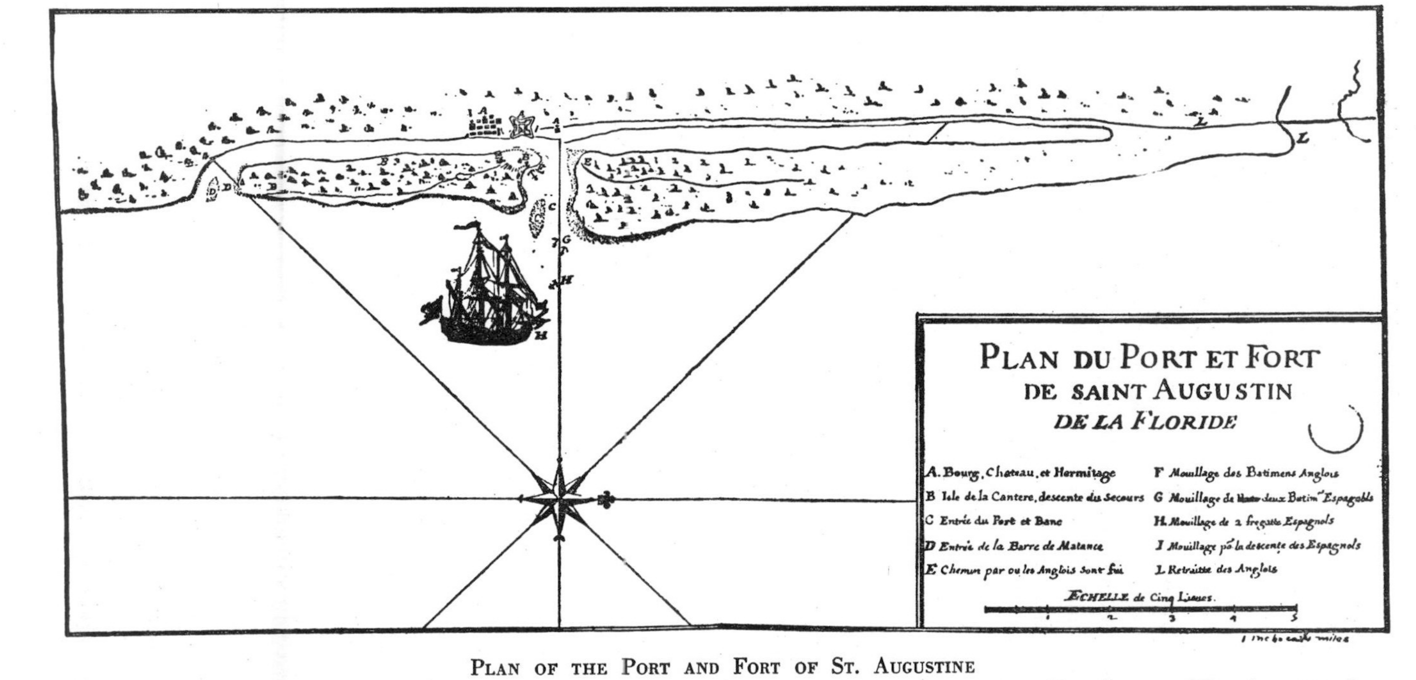

PLAN OF THE PORT AND FORT OF ST. AUGUSTINE

Anchorages and troop movements in the St. Augustine campaign are shown on this contemporary French map. The siege trenches around the fort are minute, but clearly present. This is a Library of Congress facsimile (WL 255) of the original map (138-4-2) in the Départment de la Marine, Paris.

TRANSLATION OF THE KEY

A—Town, castle, and church.
B—Island of the quarry; approach of reinforcements.
C—Entrance to the port and the bar.
D—Entrance to Matanzas Bar.
E—Trail by which the English [Moore] left.
F—Anchorage of the English vessels.
G—Anchorage of two Spanish vessels.
H—Anchorage of two Spanish frigates.
I—Anchorage for debarkation of the Spaniards.
L—Retreat of the English [Daniel].

while Berroa's fleet had sailed back north, blocking the exit. Moore, therefore, gave up the idea of a sea escape. Hurriedly he landed his own men at Vilano Beach, setting two brigantines and two sloops afire about eight o'clock that night, and abandoning in despair three sloops and one brigantine. Moore's forces with about 500 men marched north along the beach until they reached the mouth of the Salamototo. The rest of the troops also got ready to retreat quickly by the overland route to the Salamototo, where they intended to join the larger contingent that had marched along the beach. As they left the town, they set the torch to every remaining house, illuminating the darkness of the night. Zúñiga immediately ordered all the fort guns fired, thinking that the concussions might stop the spread of the flames. Although the attempt was not fully successful, Zúñiga insisted that "with the discharge of the artillery the fire diminished and some [houses] escaped [destruction]." By noon of December 30 no Englishman was visible and the flames had been checked. For the first time in months the gates of the fort opened wide. The siege was over. The fort was still Spanish, but St. Augustine was in ashes (*102, 103, 114, 137,* fols. 10434-10432, *9*).

The governor now ordered patrols organized to survey the town damage, dismantle the English siege works that surrounded the fort, and collect all war matériel left by the enemy. The demolition was undertaken by the seventy Galician recruits, in order to rest the veterans of the siege (*102*). The men found that the English had practically destroyed the town. Adjutant Joseph Rodríguez related that the fire had burned all the houses, including the main church, the Franciscan friary and its chapel, the governor's palace, the houses of the accountant and the treasurer, plus the chapel of Nuestra Señora de la Leche at Nombre de Dios. According to the adjutant, only the chapel of Nuestra Señora de la Soledad remained standing (*29,* fol. 12452; *30,* fols. 2847, 3568).

Father Martín de Alacano, in charge of the Indian mission of Nombre de Dios, said that the English destroyed everything "with the exception of the hospital and twenty houses." He later said that the English used "furor and rancor" when setting the fire. They were especially ferocious "when burning the parochial church of St. Augustine, the church and convent of San Francisco, the *doctrina* [mission] of Nombre de Dios, and six other *doctrinas*." The Father said that "the fire was so voracious that nothing, not even a vestige, was left of these

churches, the convent, and the *doctrinas* because the construction, including the roofs and fences, was of wood." Six other witnesses supported the statement of Father de Alacano. Captain Manuel Ramírez declared that the chapel of the hospital, Nuestra Señora de la Soledad, was not burned to the ground but was badly damaged. According to him the English had left intact only "about twenty houses of no value." Juan de Urrutia reported that the Soledad chapel was only slightly damaged; Ensign Juan Machado stated that the chapel was severely burned,

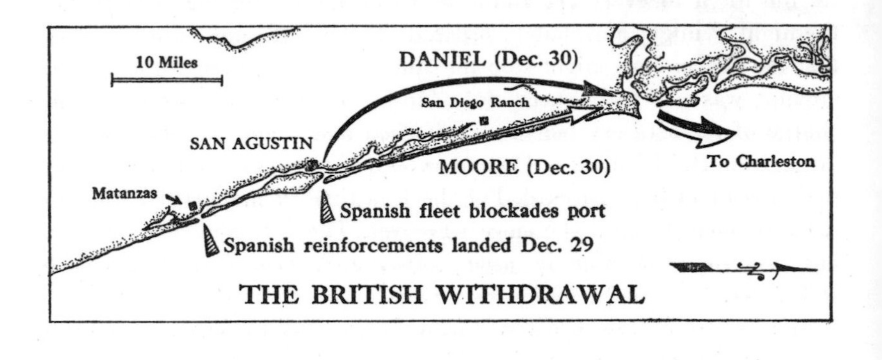

THE BRITISH WITHDRAWAL

but the English had left standing "twenty or thirty houses," and the ashes of the friary smoldered for many days. Antonio Sánches de Andrade Vaamonde wrote that "approximately twenty or twenty-five houses were left" (*141,* fols. 5090-5072). The Council of War in 1703 said that all St. Augustine had been burned to the ground and "only the hospital and some twenty damaged houses remained. All the others were burned, especially the parochial church, the monastery of St. Francis, the mission of Nombre de Dios and six other missions, without a sign of them left since they were built of wood." To the king the Council also reported: "to this harm was added the great disaster of the enemy's having burned all the farms and plantings and destroyed the cattle and crops" (*140*).

The appraisal made several years later showed that 118 persons lost houses at the hands of the English. How many houses this included is unknown, because some proprietors had more than one house, and the list mentions only their accumulated value. The cheapest house burned belonged to Diego Carvallo and was appraised at 80 pesos "because it was the oldest one." Alonso Bernal's house was valued at 100 pesos

because it was of "straw and wood." (It was a wooden house with thatched roof.) The most expensive building destroyed by the English fire was the governor's residence appraised at 8,000 pesos. The residences of the accountant Pueyo and of Captain Pedro Horruytiner were listed at 1,500 pesos each, while the one belonging to the Zigarroa family was 200 pesos less in value. Captain Joachim de Florencia lost two houses which were appraised at 3,000 pesos. The Ponce de León family claimed the loss of three houses valued at 2,200 pesos; and the heirs of ex-Governor Pablo de Hita Salazar reported the destruction of one house that was marked at 1,000 pesos. The total appraised value of Spanish property destroyed by the English fire came to 47,140 pesos (*142*).

The siege was finished, the English had failed to achieve their goal and had retreated ingloriously, losing much matériel but few men. St. Augustine was in ashes and the work of reconstruction lay ahead. The task would take a long time, so long that the main church was not rebuilt until the second Spanish period (*133*). The days right after the siege were absorbed in a loud controversy between Governor Zúñiga and General Berroa, commander of the relief fleet. The two men disagreed violently about several issues. First Zúñiga was at a loss to understand Berroa's exact duty and responsibility, since Captain López de Solloso was in charge of the relief force. Second, Zúñiga accused the general of having failed to destroy the English ships. Third, Berroa had looted the abandoned English ships without giving a share to the St. Augustine garrison who had valiantly fought the enemy. Fourth, Berroa had coldly turned down Zúñiga's request to leave some of the fleet to reinforce the garrison, especially in view of the expected arrival of Colonel Daniel from Jamaica. Fifth, Berroa even refused to leave one large ship or some small launches for the same protection. Sixth, Berroa had opposed the landing of his two well-trained colored companies (*pardos* and *morenos*), to offer battle to the English and destroy them. Instead the youngest and weakest soldiers were landed and they became panicky upon facing the enemy, who were thus able to escape. This was confirmed by the ecclesiatic visitor, Antonio Ponce de León. Seventh, the general had been extremely discourteous, never coming ashore, refusing conferences, failing to answer memorandums and sailing away with part of the fleet without notice on January 8. Eighth, and finally, Zúñiga was very incensed with Berroa for not pursuing the enemy northward with fresh troops and powerful ships,

thereby missing the chance of a great victory. In summary, Governor Zúñiga was furiously angry at Berroa, and with apparently good reasons (*103* through *129*; *30*, fol. 3247).

Once convinced that he could do nothing with Berroa, Zúñiga decided to call several meetings of his staff officers to discuss whether the English should be pursued by the St. Augustine forces. The governor was in favor of such an offensive, but in a January 3 meeting attended by Captains José Vegambre, Joachim de Florencia, Juan Benedit Horruytiner, Juan Ruis Mexía, Francisco Menéndez, Diego Díaz de Mexía, Francisco Romo de Urisa, Ensign Antonio Díaz Mexía, and chief aide-de-camp Bernardo Nieto de Carvajal, the majority voted against Zúñiga's proposal. Only Romo de Urisa and Nieto de Carvajal, the governor's favorite, sided with Zúñiga. The others thought the garrison too exhausted, the English already too far north; and there was too much danger in leaving the fort unprotected. Absent from this meeting, which Zúñiga said was attended exclusively by *criollos* (all American-born officers), were Joseph Benedit Horruytiner, Adjutant Sebastián López de Toledo, and the sick and feeble sergeant major, Enrique Primo de Rivera. Zúñiga was quite discouraged about the vote but decided to accept the advice of his men. However, he ordered Captain Joseph Horruytiner to take forty of the young Galicians north to the nearby island of Camacho and the little ranch (*hato*) of San Diego "on this side of the bar of San Juan," for it was said that the enemy had left Spanish prisoners and arms behind. The contingent never reached its destination because, according to relief Captain Joseph Primo de Rivera, the Galicians were so exhausted from their duties and the bitter cold of the past days that many collapsed on the sand. Zúñiga was furious at the lack of preparation of these recruits who couldn't even march (*107, 108, 109, 112*).

Another meeting was held on January 7 with the same officers plus Joseph Horruytiner, Enrique Primo de Rivera, and Adjutant López de Toledo. Zúñiga again criticized General Berroa severely for his behavior. The council requested Captain López de Solloso to reinforce the weak garrison. Afterwards Zúñiga sent Solloso an order to furnish "within two hours the names of an additional eighty soldiers who will temporarily remain at the fort." Solloso responded that he could supply only thirty men from his relief force. Quite reluctantly the governor accepted this number, and had the thirty men sign the payroll (*122, 123, 124, 125, 126, 128*). The next day Berroa sailed away. We have no

record on the departure of Solloso except a provision list dated March 14, 1703, of the "infantry of the city of Havana" (*134, 135*).

With the departure of Berroa the story of the siege came to an end. The English governor reached Charleston with his army in good condition. The English sources say he had only two casualties, although the Spanish Council of War in Madrid reported that Zúñiga's force "killed more than sixty men, not counting the ones the artillery blew to pieces." The Council also announced that Spanish casualties were "3 or 4 dead and 20 wounded" (*19*, p. 344, *138*). The reliability of both English and Spanish reports is questionable. Though the English casualties were low, Governor Moore nevertheless became discredited and lost his governorship. He badly wanted revenge for his defeat, and in 1704 he marched into Apalachee, bringing destruction and death (*8*).

Governor Zúñiga's reputation increased. On January 4, 1703, he rendered preliminary testimony on the siege to Antonio Ponce de León, the *visitador general eclesiástico,* and Manuel Quiñones, the visiting public notary, both of whom had come from Havana (*114, 129*). Two days later the governor wrote a condensed report of the siege for the attention of the crown (*9*). Eventually Zúñiga was rewarded with the more important and desirable governorship of Cartagena, leaving St. Augustine on April 9, 1706 (*30*, fol. 3280). The new executive, Francisco Córcoles y Martínez, conducted the *residencia,* or official review of his administration. In the *residencia* the two royal officials, Juan de Pueyo and Juan Benedit Horruytiner, blamed the ex-governor for the destruction of St. Augustine, saying that he avoided an open battle and retreated into the fort (*29*, fols. 13086-13077). The *residencia* included over 1,400 folios, wherein the official records of the English attack were transcribed (*29, 30*). These folios were the major source for this monograph. Zúñiga's tactics were accepted as sound however, and the ex-governor was completely vindicated. By Zúñiga's choice, St. Augustine was destroyed but kept Spanish. Otherwise the town might have been saved, but it would have become English. Obviously the Spanish authorities preferred destruction and retention of sovereignty. A Pyrrhic victory had been won.

BIBLIOGRAPHY

PRINTED SOURCES

1. ALMIRANTE, José. *Diccionario militar.* Madrid, 1869.
2. ARANA, Luis. "Infantry in Spanish Florida, 1671-1679," seminar paper, History 778, University of Florida, 1958. 38 pp.
3. ARCHDALE, John. *A New Description of That Fertile and Pleasant Province of Carolina, 1707,* in Alexander S. Salley, Jr., (ed.), *Narratives of Early Carolina, 1650-1708.* New York, 1911, pp. 282-311.
4. ASH, John. *The Present State of affairs in Carolina, 1706,* in Salley, 3, pp. 269-276.
5. BARADO, Francisco. *Historia del Ejército Español.* Vol. III. Barcelona [ca. 1883].
6. BOLTON, Herbert E. *Arredondo's Historical Proof of Spain's Title to Georgia.* Berkeley, 1925.
7. BOYD, Mark F. (ed.). "Documents. Further Considerations of the Apalachee Missions," *The Americas,* IX, 4 (1953), 459-479.
8. BOYD, Mark F., Hale G. Smith, and John W. Griffin. *Here They Once Stood.* Gainesville, 1951.
9. BOYD, Mark F., translator. "The Siege of Saint Augustine by Governor Moore of South Carolina in 1702 as Reported to the King of Spain by Don Joseph de Zúñiga y Zerda, Governor of Florida," *Florida Historical Quarterly,* XXVI, 4 (1948), 345-352.
10. CRANE, Verner W. "The Southern Frontier in Queen Anne's War," *American Historical Review,* XXIV (1918-1919), 379-395.
11. ———. *The Southern Frontier, 1670-1732.* Ann Arbor, 1929 and 1956.
12. DUNKLE, John R. "Population Change as an Element in the Historical Geography of St. Augustine," *Florida Historical Quarterly,* XXXVII, 1 (1958), 3-32.
13. GEIGER, Maynard. *Biographical Dictionary of the Franciscans in Spanish Florida and Cuba (1528-1841).* Paterson, N. J., 1940.
14. JOHNSON, James Guyton. "The Colonial Southeast, 1732-1763; an International Contest for Territorial and Economic Control," *The University of Colorado Studies,* XIX, 3 (1932), 163-225.
15. LAWSON, Edward W. *The Discovery of Florida and Its Discoverer, Juan Ponce de León.* St. Augustine, 1946.
16. MANUCY, Albert C. *Artillery through the Ages.* Washington, 1949.
17. ———. *The Building of the Castillo de San Marcos.* Washington, 1942.
18. ———(ed.). *The History of Castillo de San Marcos and Fort Matanzas.* Washington, 1945.
19. OLDMIXON, John. *From the History of the British Empire in America, 1708,* in Salley, 3, pp. 317-373.
20. *Primera y breve relación de las favorables noticias que con fechas de seis y veinte y ocho de enero de este año de 1703, se han tenido por cartas de don Luis de Zúñiga, Governador de la Florida y D. Luis Chacón, Governador de la Havana.* Madrid: Antonio Bizarrón [1703] , 2 pp., in John Carter Brown Library.
21. RAMSAY, David. *The History of South Carolina from Its First Settlement in 1670 to the Year 1808.* Charleston, 1809.

22. Rubio y Bellve, Mariano. *Diccionario de ciencias militares.* 3 vols. Barcelona, 1895-1901.
23. Salley, A. S. (ed.). *Journals of the Commons House of Assembly of South Carolina for 1702.* Columbia, S. C., 1932.
24. ———(ed.). *Journals of the Commons House of Assembly of South Carolina for 1703.* Columbia, S. C., 1934.
25. Shea, John Gilmary. *History of the Catholic Church in the United States.* Akron, Ohio [1886].
26. Soto y Abbach, Serafín María de, Conde de Clonard. *Historia orgánica de las armas de infantería y caballería españoles desde la creación del ejército permanente hasta el día.* 16 vols. Madrid, 1851-1859.
27. TePaske, John J. "Economic Problems of Florida Governors, 1700-1763," *Florida Historical Quarterly,* XXXVII, 1 (1958), pp. 42-52.
28. Wallace, Duncan David. *The History of South Carolina.* Vol. I. New York, 1934.

TWO PRINCIPAL LEGAJOS

(The following documents are available in the Stetson Collection, University of Florida.)

29. Demanda Puesta Por Los Señores Juezes offiziales de la Real Hazienda Contra el Exmo. Señor Maestro de Campo General, Don Joseph de Zúñiga y La Zerda; Governador de Cartagena Sobre Diferentes Capítulos y Cargos. Juez de Residencia, Francisco Córcoles y Martínez; Escribano Público y de Gobernación, Juan Solana. St. Augustine, 1707. AGI, 58-2-8, 849 fols.
30. Residencia de Don Joseph de Zúñiga y la Zerda. Quaderno 4° de Cargos, Descargos y Sentenzias. Juez de Residencia, Francisco Córcoles y Martínez; Escribano Público y de Gobernación, Juan Solana. St. Augustine, Feb. 11, 1707. AGI, 58-2-8, 593 fols.

CHRONOLOGICAL LIST OF DOCUMENTS CONSULTED

(Unless otherwise noted, the following documents are available in the Stetson Collection, University of Florida.)

31. Obispo de Cuba to the crown. Havana, Sept. 28, 1689. With enclosures. AGI, 54-2-2, 6 fols.
32. The royal officials [Joachin de Florencia and Juan de Pueyo] to the crown. St. Augustine, Sept. 2, 1699. With enclosures. AGI, 54-5-15, 20 fols.
33. Governor Zúñiga to the crown. St. Augustine, March 15, 1702. With enclosures. AGI, 58-1-27. (Available on microfilm, roll 9, North Carolina Spanish Records, in the Library of Florida History, University of Florida.)
34. Francisco Romo de Uriza to Governor Zúñiga. San Luis [Apalachee], Oct. 22, 1702. In 7, pp. 470-472.
35. Manuel Solana to Governor Zúñiga. San Luis [Apalachee], Oct. 22, 1702. In 7, pp. 468-470.
36. Governor Zúñiga, Auto. St. Augustine, Oct. 27, 1702. In 29, fols. 13069-13067.
37. Governor Zúñiga to [the crown]. St. Augustine, Nov. 1, 1702. In 29, fols. 12634-12632.
38. Governor Zúñiga to Manuel Solana. St. Augustine, Nov. 1, 1702. In 29, fols. 13052-13051.

39. The governor and royal officials of Florida to the governor and royal officials of Havana. St. Augustine, Nov. 1, 1702. In 29, fols. 12631-12628.
40. Francisco Fuentes to Governor Zúñiga. San Juan [del Puerto, Guale], Nov. 4, 1702. In 29, fols. 13042-13041.
41. Governor Zúñiga, Auto. St. Augustine, Nov. 5, 1702. In 29, fols. 13058-13053.
42. Governor Zúñiga, Auto. St. Augustine, Nov. 5, 1702. In 29, fols. 13050-13046.
43. Governor Zúñiga, Auto. St. Augustine, Nov. 5, 1702. In 29, fols. 13045-13044.
44. [Governor Zúñiga] to the crown. St. Augustine, Nov. 5, 1702. In 29, fols. 12627-12625.
45. The governor and royal officials of Florida to the governor and royal officials of Cuba. St. Augustine, Nov. 5, 1702. In 29, fols. 12624-12623.
46. Governor Zúñiga, Auto. St. Augustine, Nov. 6, 1702. In 29, fols. 13040-13033.
47. Governor Zúñiga, Auto. St. Augustine, Nov. 6, 1702. In 29, fols. 13031-13030.
48. Governor Zúñiga, Auto. St. Augustine, Nov. 7, 1702. In 29, fols. 13028-13024.
49. Governor Zúñiga to [Manuel Solana]. St. Augustine, Nov. 7, 1702. In 29, fol. 13023.
50. Declaration of Captain Diego de la Sierra. St. Augustine, Nov. 8, 1702. In 29, fols. 13012-13010.
51. Declaration of Diego Gutiérrez. St. Augustine, Nov. 8, 1702. In 29, fols. 13003-13002.
52. Declaration of Martín Sánchez. St. Augustine, Nov. 8, 1702. In 29, fols. 13008-13006.
53. Declaration of Pedro Belén. St. Augustine, Nov. 8, 1702. In 29, fols. 13010-13008.
54. Governor Zúñiga, Auto. St. Augustine, Nov. 8, 1702. In 29, fols. 13022-13019.
55. Governor Zúñiga, Auto. St. Augustine, Nov. 8, 1702. In 29, fols. 13016-13015.
56. Governor Zúñiga, Auto. St. Augustine, Nov. 8, 1702. In 29, fols. 13014-13013.
57. Governor Zúñiga, Auto. St. Augustine, Nov. 8, 1702. In 29, fol. 13001.
58. Acuerdo of the governor and royal officials. St. Augustine, Nov. 9, 1702. In 29, fols. 13001-12997.
59. Acuerdo of the governor and royal officials. St. Augustine, Nov. 9, 1702. In 29, fols. 12961-12959.
60. Declaration of Joseph Williams. St. Augustine, Nov. 9, 1702. In 29, fols. 12995-12988.
61. Declaration of Manuel Agramón. St. Augustine, Nov. 9, 1702. In 29, fols. 12980-12977.
62. Declaration of William Nobel. St. Augustine, Nov. 9, 1702. In 29, fols. 12987-12980.
63. Enrique Primo de Rivera to Governor Zúñiga. St. Augustine, Nov. 9, 1702. In 29, fols. 12969-12967.
64. Governor Zúñiga, Auto. St. Augustine, Nov. 9, 1702. In 29, fols. 12976-12973.
65. Governor Zúñiga, Auto. St. Augustine, Nov. 9, 1702. In 29, fols. 12972-12970.
66. Governor Zúñiga, Auto. St. Augustine, Nov. 9, 1702. In 29, fols. 12966-12964.
67. Governor Zúñiga, Auto. St. Augustine, Nov. 9, 1702. In 29, fol. 12962.
68. Governor Zúñiga, Auto. St. Augustine, Nov. 10, 1702. In 29, fols. 12958-12954.
69. Governor Zúñiga, Auto. St. Augustine, Nov. 10, 1702. In 29, fols. 12953-12950.
70. Governor Zúñiga, Auto. St. Augustine, Nov. 10, 1702. In 29, fols. 12949-12946.
71. Governor Zúñiga, Auto. St. Augustine, Nov. 10, 1702. In 29, fols. 12945-12943.
72. Governor Zúñiga, Auto. St. Augustine, Nov. 10, 1702. In 29, fols. 12941-12938.
73. Governor Zúñiga to Manuel Solana. San Luis [Apalachee], Nov. 10, 1702. In 29, fols. 12937-12936.

74. Governor Zúñiga, Auto. St. Augustine, Nov. 11, 1702. In 29, fols. 12935-12932.
75. John Martin [Juan Martín] to Governor James Moore. [Nombre de Dios], Nov. 12, 1702. Original and translated version in 29, fols. 12918-12915.
76. Manuel Solana to Governor Zúñiga. San Luis [Apalachee], Nov. 13, 1702. In 29, fols. 12885-12883.
77. Diego de Jaen [Xaen] to Governor Zúñiga. Santa Fé [Timucua], Nov. 14, 1702. In 29, fol. 12890.
78. Governor Zúñiga, Auto. St. Augustine, Nov. 14, 1702. In 29, fols. 12931-12929.
79. Governor Zúñiga, Auto. St. Augustine, Nov. 16, 1702. In 29, fols. 12928-12925.
80. Governor Zúñiga, Auto. St. Augustine, Nov. 22, 1702. In 29, fols. 12924-12922.
81. Bernardo Nieto Carvajal, Notificación, St. Augustine, Nov. 23, 1702. In 29, fols. 12916-12915.
82. Declaration of John Day [Juan Día]. St. Augustine, Nov. 23, 1702. In 29, fols. 12907-12904.
83. Declaration of Thomas Jones [Tomás Fonei]. St. Augustine, Nov. 23, 1702. In 29, fols. 12913-12908.
84. Governor Zúñiga, Auto. St. Augustine, Nov. 23, 1702. In 29, fols. 12921-12920.
85. Juan Solana, Notificación. St. Augustine, Nov. 23, 1702. In 29, fol. 12910.
86. Governor Zúñiga, Auto. St. Augustine, Nov. 25, 1702. In 29, fols. 12903-12900.
87. Francisco Fuentes de Galarza to Governor Zúñiga. No place, no date (received in St. Augustine on Nov. 28, 1702). In 29, fols. 12896-12894.
88. Governor Zúñiga, Auto. St. Augustine, Nov. 28, 1702. In 29, fols. 12899-12897.
89. Diego de Florencia, Receipt. Santa María de Galve [Pensacola], Dec. 2, 1702. In 29, fol. 12603.
90. Governor Zúñiga, Auto. St. Augustine, Dec. 2, 1702. In 29, fols. 12892-12891.
91. Pedro Nicolás Benítez de Lugo, Auto. Havana, Dec. 2, 1702. In 29, fols. 12828-12825.
92. Juan Clemente Horruytiner to Governor Zúñiga. [Some place along the St. Johns River, about Dec. 6, 1702.] In 29, fol. 12879.
93. Governor Zúñiga, Auto. St. Augustine, Dec. 11, 1702. In 29, fols. 12882-12879.
94. Governor Zúñiga, Auto. St. Augustine, Dec. 14, 1702. In 29, fols. 12878-12875.
95. Governor Zúñiga, Auto. St. Augustine, Dec. 19, 1702. In 29, fols. 12874-12871.
96. Manuel Solana, Auto. San Luis [Apalachee], Dec. 20, 1702. In Boyd 8, pp. 38-39.
97. Michael Cole to Mr. William Blathwayte. Carolina, Dec. 22, 1702. In Vol. 306, Colonial Office 5, Public Record Office, London (copy at the St. Augustine Historical Society).
98. Governor Zúñiga, Auto. St. Augustine, Dec. 24, 1702. In 29, fols. 12870-12867.
99. Governor Zúñiga, Auto. St. Augustine, Dec. 25, 1702. In 29, fols. 12866-12863.
100. Governor Zúñiga, Auto. St. Augustine, Dec. 26, 1702. In 29, fols. 12862-12860.
101. Governor Zúñiga, Auto. St. Augustine, Dec. 27, 1702. In 29, fols. 12859-12854.
102. Governor Zúñiga, Auto. St. Augustine, Dec. 30, 1702. In 29, fols. 12853-12850.
103. Governor Zúñiga, Auto. St. Augustine, Dec. 31, 1702. In 29, fols. 12849-12846.
104. Governor Zúñiga, Auto. St. Augustine, Jan. 1, 1703. In 29, fols. 12845-12842.
105. Estevan de Berroa to Governor Zúñiga. [Aboard the "Black Eagle"], Jan. 2, 1703. In 29, fols. 12838-12837.
106. Governor Zúñiga, Auto. St. Augustine, Jan. 2, 1703. In 29, fols. 12841-12839.
107. Governor Zúñiga, Auto. St. Augustine, Jan. 3, 1703. In 29, fols. 12836-12835.
108. Governor Zúñiga, Auto. St. Augustine, Jan. 3, 1703. In 29, fols. 12831-12829.
109. Pareceres de la Junta de Guerra. St. Augustine [Jan. 3, 1703]. In 29, fols. 12834-12832.

110. Declaration of Diego Caro. St. Augustine, Jan. 4, 1703. In 29, fols. 12786-12783.
111. Declaration of Francisco Basurtto. St. Augustine, Jan. 4, 1703. In 29, fols. 12783-12780.
112. Declaration of Joseph Primo de Ribera. St. Augustine, Jan. 4, 1703. In 29, fols. 12774-12771.
113. Governor Zúñiga, Auto. St. Augustine, Jan. 4, 1703. In 29, fols. 12824-12821.
114. Governor Zúñiga, Auto suplicatorio. St. Augustine, Jan. 4, 1703. In 29, fols. 12789-12786.
115. Declaration of Sebastián López de Tholedo. St. Augustine, Jan. 4, 1703. In 29, fols. 12779-12774.
116. Anthonio Ponze de León, Auto. St. Augustine, Jan. 5, 1703. In 29, fols. 12768-12766.
117. Anthonio Ponze de León, Certificación. St. Augustine, Jan. 5, 1703. In 29, fols. 12771-12768.
118. Pareceres de la Junta de la Guerra. St. Augustine [Jan. 5, 1703]. In 29, fols. 12820-12817.
119. Governor Zúñiga, Auto. St. Augustine, Jan. 6, 1703. In 29, fols. 12815-12814.
120. Opinion of Esteban de Berroa signed by Sebastián López de Toledo. St. Augustine, Jan. 6, 1703. In 29, fol. 12816.
121. Pareceres de la Junta de Guerra. St. Augustine [Jan. 6, 1703]. In 29, fols. 12813-12810.
122. Governor Zúñiga, Auto. St. Augustine, Jan. 7, 1703. In 29, fols. 12808-12805.
123. Governor Zúñiga, Auto. St. Augustine, Jan. 7, 1703. In 29, fols. 12800-12799.
124. Governor Zúñiga, Auto. St. Augustine, Jan. 7, 1703. In 29, fols. 12797-12796.
125. Governor Zúñiga to López Solloso. St. Augustine, Jan. 7, 1703. In 29, fols. 12799-12798.
126. Governor Zúñiga to Manuel Ramírez. St. Augustine, Jan. 7, 1703. In 29, fol. 12797.
127. Opinion of Esteban de Berroa. [Aboard the "Black Eagle"], Jan. 7, 1703. In 29, fol. 12809.
128. Pareceres de la Junta de Guerra. St. Augustine, Jan. 7, 1703. In 29, fols. 12804-12801.
129. Governor Zúñiga, Auto. St. Augustine, Jan. 9, 1703. In 29, fols. 12791-12790.
130. Diego de Florencia to Governor Zúñiga. San Luis [Apalachee], Jan. 25, 1703. In Boyd, 8, pp. 39-40.
131. Fray Marcos de Sotolongo to the crown. Havana, Jan. 30, 1703. AGI, 58-2-14, 3 fols.
132. Manuel Solana to Governor Zúñiga. San Luis [Apalachee], Feb. 3, 1703. In Boyd, 8, pp. 41-42.
133. Fray Marcos de Sotolongo to the governor of Florida. No place, Feb. 27, 1703. In 29, fol. 12423.
134. Governor Zúñiga, Auto. St. Augustine, March 1, 1703. In 29, fol. 12745.
135. Statistics of Francisco de Veles, Escrivano de raziones y muniziones. St. Augustine, March 14, 1703. In 29, fols. 12744-12742.
136. Governor Zúñiga, Auto. St. Augustine, March 16, 1703. In 29, fol. 12741.
137. Duque de Albuquerque, Virrey, to the crown. México, April 10, 1703. AGI, 58-1-27, 110 fols.
138. Pareceres de la Junta de Guerra. Madrid, May 22, 1703. AGI, 58-1-23, 2 fols. (Available on microfilm, roll 9, North Carolina Spanish Records, University of Florida.)

139. Jacinto Roque Pérez to Governor Zúñiga. San Luis [Apalachee], May 25, 1703. In Boyd, 8, pp. 42-44.
140. Pareceres de la Junta de Guerra. Madrid, July 6, 1703. AGI, 58-1-23, 4 fols. (Available on microfilm, roll 9, North Carolina Spanish Records, University of Florida.)
141. Memorial de Fray Martín de Alacano. Madrid, Aug. 2, 1703. AGI, 58-2-14, 121 fols.
142. Francisco de Córcoles y Martínez to the crown. With enclosures. St. Augustine, Aug. 13, 1709. AGI, 58-1-28, 28 fols. (Available on microfilm, roll 12, North Carolina Spanish Records, University of Florida.)
143. Governor Zúñiga to the crown. Cartagena, June 3, 1710. With enclosures. AGI, 58-1-28, 19 fols.
144. Juan de Pueyo and Juan Benedit Horruytiner, royal officials [Accusations of]. St. Augustine, no date. In 29, fols. 13086-13077.

UNIVERSITY OF FLORIDA MONOGRAPHS

Social Sciences

No. 1 (Winter 1959) : ***The Whigs of Florida, 1845-1854***
By Herbert J. Doherty, Jr.

No. 2 (Spring 1959) : ***Austrian Catholics and the Social Question, 1918-1932***
By Alfred Diamant

No. 3 (Summer 1959) : ***The Siege of St. Augustine in 1702***
By Charles W. Arnade

Made in the USA
Columbia, SC
13 February 2019

PROLOGUE

"Get out and don't ever come back!"

Clint couldn't believe what he was hearing. How could his wife be so angry with him? Sure, he had cheated before. But each time he was caught, he was able to alter his ways long enough for her to change her mind and let him stay.

It was different this time. Not only had he been caught in his most recent affair but had that woman with him when he wrecked his pickup and got arrested for driving under the influence. His lawyer told him since it was his third DUI, he may have to spend a few months in jail and he was sure to lose his driver's license permanently, though it had already

been temporarily suspended. Life was spinning out of control. Clint had never felt so lost.

Clint didn't see himself as being that different from other hands on the ranch. Most of the men he knew liked to drink and several of them ran around on their wives. It was true he took his fun to a higher degree than most. In fact, he partied most weekends and even a few evenings during the week. He is about average in height with a ruddy complexion and a hawk-like nose. His rugged good looks brought out a vanity that caused him to never miss a chance to check himself out in a mirror. He knew he was attractive to women and took advantage of it.

He guessed things got worse when he realized he could get a nice high on pills without having to hear his wife tell him he smelled like a brewery. At first, he just did the pills a few days each week. Before long he was using every day. They didn't affect his work so far as he knew. He was able to keep a little buzz going without being noticeably under the influence. In the evenings he would drink, usually at one of the several bars in Bandera.

* * * * * * *

Bandera is not a big city. The population, according to the sign at the edge of town, is 957. The city keeps a pretty careful count as families move in and move out, but the population has remained stable for decades. It is called the "Cowboy Capital of the World" because it claims to have more world champion cowboys as residents than any other city and also because of the large number of dude ranches in the area. It didn't become an incorporated city until 1964 and remains the only incorporated city in the county by the same name.

The name Bandera is Spanish for "flag." Polish immigrants founded it in the mid-1800s. Located in the Texas Hill Country, it is about fifty miles northwest of San Antonio. Known for hot, humid summers, the unrelenting heat could fry an egg on the sidewalk on most days in the summer. But the spring and fall months are so temperate that this remains one of the most popular destinations in Texas.

Main Street is the site of most of the city's businesses. In a several block stretch, stores sell antiques, western wear, auto parts, and barbecue, and assorted cafés sell steaks, Mexican food, as well as Chinese and Italian food; along with a washeteria, several banks, and as many churches—

though most of the churches are relegated to the side streets. There is a dollar store, a Christmas store (must be a popular holiday in this town), even more banks (do people have so much money here that they need more banks?), hardware stores, a car wash, liquor stores, country stores, general stores (what's the difference?), a few gas stations, several pharmacies, some paint and body shops (they stay very busy fixing the many vehicles that have collided with one of the abundant deer in the area), realty offices that advertise ranches for sale, a taxidermist or two, and more fast food restaurants than can be counted. There is also a library, post office, museum, fire department, and city offices. All of this is in a downtown area that is no more than a mile long. But if you look for the police department, you will not find it because the city council decided since Bandera is the Cowboy Capital of the World, they should rename it the Marshal's Office. So instead of a police chief, the city has a marshal. Instead of police officers, there are deputy marshals. There is no jail, so the marshal's office uses the county jail at the county Justice Center. In front of the marshal's office is a planter that is made to look like a well-worn cowboy boot. It looks right at home in this western town.

In the general store downtown there is often a local musician playing and singing. Sometimes the only people in the store are the musician's wife and the storekeeper—but he plays with gusto as though a thousand adoring fans are listening. Recently, he was joined by a guitarist from Wisconsin who fell in love with the area and stayed, not for the day as he planned, but for three weeks. He comes in the general store and puts out a tip jar and plays for hours, often for no tips. Then he goes to the local RV park and plays and collects fifteen to twenty dollars in an evening of entertainment. He was happy and so were those who comprised his tiny audience.

The courthouse was built in 1890 from locally quarried stone. It has been the center of town life since it was built but today only has a couple of people who office there. The cupola on the courthouse features clock faces on all four sides. However, the structure has never contained a clock. All four faces are painted so it appears to be perpetually ten minutes after ten o'clock. Today, most of the offices as well as court functions have been relocated to the Bandera County Justice Center located a few miles out of town.

Even though the old courtroom is seldom used, it still has rules posted:

1. Dress Code
    a. No shirts with inappropriate languages or images. (One wonders if languages other than English are not allowed.)
    b. Shoes must be worn.
    c. No hats or caps worn in the courtroom.
    d. No plunging necklines, open backs, or strapless shirts.
    e. No exposed midriffs.
    f. No shorts above knee length or cutoffs allowed.
2. Cell phones, pagers, and electronic devices must be turned off completely before entering the courtroom.
3. No show of affection in the courtroom.
4. No cameras or recording equipment in the courtroom.
5. No food or drink in the courtroom.

Any person violating these rules is subject to being held in Contempt of Court.

Clearly, Bandera takes court seriously.

CHAPTER 1: PATIENCE

"Patience is waiting. Not passively waiting.
That is laziness.
But to keep going when the going
is hard and slow – that is patience."
~ Unknown

Cowboy. For some it is a term of derision. It's used to indicate someone was not known for taking stock of a situation but would just react and "cowboy" his way through. For others, it is used to indicate a person who was not yet full-grown and a bit less than a mature man. But, to the many who have ridden the range now or in generations past, cowboy is a name to be proud of; a word that conveys a person is a rugged individual who has a sense of pride and an even deeper sense of integrity. A true cowboy is not someone who wears fancy jeans or western store shirts that come out of Hollywood. Real cowboys—Texas cowboys—work from before dawn until after dusk for little pay, building fence, caring for cattle, and upholding the code of the old west—the code of their forefathers. They are men who have adapted to the necessity of embracing modern

technology, but will gladly park their pickups and holster their cell phones as they saddle up for another long day on horseback doing work they love.

Today's cowboy is a blend of renaissance man, pioneer, jack-of-all-trades, and good ole boy. Some make fun of him. Others envy him. But what today's cowboy knows is, ranches can't run without him and his kind. Today's cowboy is a dying breed but also a resilient creature who delights in giving a hard day's work and is known to tip back a few cold ones after the sun goes down.

Meet Clint Hazard. He's a modern-day cowboy who believes he was born one hundred and fifty years too late. He daydreams about living in the old west, when things were simpler, where the measure of a man was in how hard and how long he worked. Clint dislikes computers, cell phones, and other forms of modern technology, though he has to use them on his work at the H&F Ranch. Everything on the ranch is inventoried and that inventory, along with every part of the ranch operation, is kept on computer. At a glance, the owners can tell how many head of cattle they have, where on the ranch they are located, how much oil is being pumped from each well, the condition of the irrigation system, and which water wells are due for pump

maintenance.

Clint is about five feet and nine inches tall. He walks with a bit of a limp thanks to being thrown too many times when he rodeoed. His face is dark brown from the many years he's spent working in the sun. He's lean to the point of being skinny and is always moving like he's full of nervous energy. Women find Clint to be ruggedly handsome—which continues to lead him into trouble. He sees himself as a good-hearted, God-fearing, family man who is a top cowboy. It is true he runs around with other women, but he still considers himself a pretty good husband.

He's smart. Clint could have completed college, but he found it hard to tone down his partying and do any studying. He flunked out after a year at Blinn College—a junior college in nearby Brenham—and moved back to Bandera. Married his high school sweetheart. Had a son within a year. His wife loved him in the past but got tired of his unfaithfulness. She didn't like the way he flirted with her friends and the off-color jokes he told in mixed company. He could be short-tempered, prone to violence, quick with his fists, but quicker with a sharp retort.

Clint is a cheater—he cheats on his wife and at cards. Always believes the deck is stacked against him. He justifies

his unfaithfulness because he's a hard-worker and a good provider. Clint is also a hard-drinker. He never drinks when he is working but knows he is not worth much many mornings after a long night of drinking and carousing. He takes pride that he can drink more than most of the other hands and still pull more than his weight when it comes to work on the ranch. Clint secretly fears what life will be like in the future. He wonders how long it will take him to completely self-destruct. At times like this, he doesn't like himself much, even though he acts like he's the most confident man around. He keeps these thoughts secret—and most of the time, he keeps them secret from himself.

Clint is good at his job. Out of seventy-five or so hands at the H&F Ranch, he feels he is among the best. And many of the younger hands look up to him. The work is hard, but he loves it.

He is the assistant to the section boss, Micah Goodfellow. They have worked side by side since arriving at the H&F. He and Micah get along well. They have known each other all their lives. When they graduated high school twenty-five years before, they both got jobs on the H&F. In the past they used to party together. They even chased women together. But some kind of change had taken place

with Micah. He's not been the same for most of the past year.

Micah has a strong enough physical resemblance to Clint that they are often asked if they're brothers. A couple of inches shorter than Clint, Micah outweighs him by several pounds. Like all the ranch hands, he's solid muscle.

Clint always thinks of himself as a cowboy's cowboy. He works harder, drinks longer, cheats with more women, and is mostly lucky any time he plays poker. Days are for working. Nights are for fun. Both are filled to capacity. But, his wife had finally had enough of his cheating and kicked him out. What's worse is that his son will not speak to him—he has to work with his son Tripp. No one had to tell Clint that Tripp was following in his footsteps. He knew Tripp partied hard and had learned it from his dad.

Clint dreaded having to tell Micah that he wrecked his pickup and his wife had kicked him out. Clint got a room in a run-down motel called Better Days Lodge. It was actually a very old motor court, held over from fifty years earlier. In the early days of Bandera, there was a hotel downtown that was called the Better Days Hotel. The rundown lodge on the edge of town held no resemblance to the once regal hotel. Clint wondered if anyone else saw the irony in the name of

the dilapidated motel. Three hundred dollars a month was more than he wanted to spend on a room, but he reasoned it was just ten bucks a night. All in all, pretty cheap accommodations. And cheap was the word for it. The room was several steps down from frugal. It was not far from where Micah lived so Clint hoped he could bum a ride to work each day since he totaled his truck and lost his license.

When Clint called Micah and told him the most recent chapter in his never-ending saga, Micah just listened and didn't say much. At the end of the conversation, Micah said, "Sure, I'll give you a ride. Not a problem. I'll be by at five in the morning."

"I'll be waiting out front. And Micah, I really 'preciate this."

"Don't mention it."

Clint should have been promoted many years before, but he continued to act like he did when he was twenty. He has a defiant streak that causes him to challenge anyone who doesn't agree with him and question most orders he's given. If it were not for the fact that he probably works harder than anyone on the ranch, he would have been fired long ago.

* * * * * * *

Clint was waiting in front of the motel Monday morning. Micah was right on time, as Clint knew he would be. Micah's old pickup didn't look like much, but it was dependable. The faded green paint and frayed seats spoke of the many years it had provided service.

"Mornin'," said Micah through the open window of the truck.

"Back at you." Clint waited for Micah to ask more about the mess he had gotten himself into. But Micah just drove. The silence hung between them for several minutes when Clint decided he owed Micah more of an explanation.

"Totaled my truck. I was coming out of the Cheer Up and didn't see the eighteen-wheeler. Didn't do much to the big rig but it sure flattened my truck. The sheriff got there and gave me a DUI and took away my license."

"Glad you weren't hurt."

"Me too. I'd hate to have to miss work. Bills are piling up now. But I guess I'm going to have to miss some work soon. My lawyer said I'll probably have to spend time in jail."

"We'll cross that bridge when we come to it. Don't worry about it now."

Micah didn't ask any questions. Clint was determined to turn over a new leaf. He wanted to give his best to his job. He knew he was letting his friend down by continuing his party life. While he knew Micah had stopped all his partying about a year before, Micah didn't preach to him. For that, Clint was grateful.

What interested Clint the most were the changes he has seen taking place in Micah's life. One of the most noticeable is the patience Micah exhibits toward him and the other hands. And Clint is not the only one to see it. The other hands have talked about it, too. In times past, Micah was short to the point of being abrupt with most hands. And for the new hires, it seemed Micah would go out of his way to show them how little they knew. He would give a new hire a job and then lash out at him if he didn't do the task just so.

Micah believed in telling a man once and expecting him to get the job done or move on and let someone else work in his place. That wasn't so uncommon for ranch foremen around Bandera. But Micah was a harder man than most.

All of that changed over the past several months. It seemed to start about the same time Micah quit partying. He didn't say much about the changes in his life except to say he had quit drinking. He said, "Drinkin' doesn't agree with me

anymore." No other explanation.

They arrived at the ranch just as the dining hall bell was being rung. That sound could be heard from more than a mile away. The on-call hands ambled out of the bunkhouse and headed toward the dining hall. The wranglers had just finished saddling the horses and they too made a beeline for the food. For breakfast, there was just the one ringing of the bell when the food was ready. But for lunch and dinner, the bell was rung thirty minutes before the meal and then again when it was time to eat.

Years ago, the dinner triangle had been replaced by an old church bell salvaged from a derelict church deep in the Texas Hill Country. It was mounted high on a post right outside the dining hall. The bell rope ran through the wall into the kitchen, so no time was wasted having to go outside to signal mealtime. The chef gave orders when the bell was to be rung.

Across the dining hall, Tripp ate his breakfast and glared at his father. He didn't say a word. The silence and the scowl on his face spoke of the contempt with which Tripp held Clint. Tripp had a bit of a chip on his shoulder most of the time. He knew it was his father's idea to name him Tripp. What parent would name his son Tripp Hazard? Tripp was

teased unmercifully throughout life, from the time roll was being checked on his first day of school until today. Whenever someone called his first and last name together, there would be an echo in the room as others repeated "Tripp Hazard," and then snickered as they had all through every grade of school.

Before Clint got kicked out of his home, he and Tripp got along pretty well. Clint was more like a friend and not much of a father. But when Tripp found out about Clint's accident and him having his girlfriend with him, he despised his father. He had known all along Clint had a wandering eye and probably slept around some. What he had not realized was how much Clint's behavior was hurting his mother. When his mother kicked Clint out of the house, Tripp phoned his father and told him he didn't want to have anything more to do with him. "When I see you at the ranch, don't expect me to speak to you. Mom and I have heard enough from you."

Clint was angry his son spoke to him like that. But more than anything, he was sad. He looked across the dining hall again at Tripp who was still scowling at him. Clint walked out of the dining hall and over to the corral fence, lit a cigarette, and waited for Micah. He wondered if he would

ever gain back the respect of his son.

"You know smokin' is going to stunt your growth."

"Listen Micah. You're not my mother or my wife. I know you quit and like my high school history teacher used to say, 'Nobody hates sinnin' like an old sinner that's quit.' But this is my life and I'll live it the way I want!"

Clint was known for having a short fuse. Today it was especially short. His confrontation with Tripp put him in a bad mood. But if it hadn't been that, it would have been something else. A day seldom passed without Clint snapping at someone.

Clint and Micah saddled up and headed for the pump house that was about a mile from the corral. They had been rebuilding the pump for the past week and hoped to get it completed today. As they rode, Clint's thoughts ran from Tripp to the job they were on to Micah and how he seemed to have mellowed over the past year. Micah still worked hard but he had more patience with himself and with others. Not once had he heard Micah swear while working on the pump. In the past, Micah could foul the air with his language as he took out his frustrations on the old pump. It needed to be replaced, not just rebuilt. But the owners wanted to get another year or two out of it before replacing it with a new

one.

They tied their horses on long leads near the pump house, so they could graze. For the next couple of hours, Clint and Micah worked on the old pump. They were mostly silent except for Clint mumbling to himself about the pump. Micah, on the other hand, seemed to be enjoying the work. Just before noon, Clint put down his tools and turned to Micah.

"I'm sorry."

"For what?"

"For jumpin' on you when you made that comment about my smokin'. I had no call to get riled at you. It just seems about anything can set me off these days."

"Forget it. I know when you are like that to just give you time and you'll get over it. I saw the way Tripp glared at you. It must hurt a lot to have your own son turn against you."

"Yeah. I deserved it. He's mainly mad I cheated on his mother. He knows I've cheated for years but me wreckin' my truck just put a spotlight on my behavior."

"I guess so. Still Tripp shouldn't treat you that way."

"Micah, I'm so mixed up. It's like my life's comin' apart in every area and there's nothin' I can do about it. The more I try to stop messin' up, the bigger mess I make. Since the

wreck, I've found myself being short with just about everyone. I snap at the other hands. I even snap at my horse and she never does anything wrong."

"Sounds like you're angry with yourself."

"But that's just it," Clint replied. "I'm not mad at anyone. It just seems that everything irritates me."

"So maybe you need to give yourself a break. Start by being patient with yourself. You've had a lot of things happen to you. Ease up on yourself."

"I think that's what I've been seein' you doin'. Why have you been so patient with the men lately? And I haven't heard you cuss even once while workin' on this worn out pump!"

Micah paused and pondered. He went back to working on the pump but remained silent for a while longer. Then he said, "I don't know how to explain it. That's not somethin' I've particularly been tryin' to do. It's just happened. I've always been hard on the men, but I am always hardest on myself. A few months ago, I decided I deserved to be treated better by me. I stopped gettin' flustered when I made a mistake or when a job didn't go the way I wanted it to go. And I realized I needed to treat the men the way I wanted to treat myself."

He continued, "So I made a deal with myself. I would

not lose patience with myself any more and I would try to treat the other men the same way. It doesn't always work. I still come down pretty hard on myself and others. But I am tryin' to change."

For the rest of the day, Clint and Micah didn't say much to each other. They concentrated on their job and worked hard to get the pump rebuild completed by dusk. Clint thought about what Micah had said and wondered if he could learn to be patient with himself and with others. He didn't see how that was possible. It just wasn't in him.

Most people can look at themselves and find things they want to change. Clint knew he needed to change his life, but he didn't know how. As he watched the changes in his friend, he contemplated how those changes had taken place.

Although he did realize the changes in the way Micah was treating people seemed to coincide with the stop in Micah's drinking, he didn't know anything about how or why Micah stopped drinking. He was not aware that Micah started attending Alcoholics Anonymous (AA) meetings the prior year and through working the program with his sponsor, he was able not only to stop his drinking but also his periodic use of narcotics and marijuana. Nor did he know Micah also realized he needed to stop running around

on his wife. While he had tried that before, he was not able to completely stop it until he quit drinking and using.

Unbeknownst to Clint, Micah was on a recovery journey, a journey that would change everything in his life. It was more than stopping drinking, using, or cheating. Recovery was a journey that would change almost everything in his life.

In meetings, Micah learned that those traits about his personality he disliked and wanted to change could be thought of as character defects. Through working the Twelve-Steps of AA, Micah was learning to identify his character defects and take measures to correct them.

The first indication he was making progress on his character defects came when Clint noticed he had become more patient. Micah was grateful and humbled that others had noticed changes in his life. He knew his work on himself was not finished. In fact, he fully believed it would take him the rest of his life—and that would not be time enough.

He wished he knew what to say to help Clint. He wanted Clint to find the hope he had found when he entered recovery. But he also knew he would have violently resisted had someone tried to get him into recovery before

he was ready. Micah was convinced he could be a positive influence on Clint, and when the time was right, Clint would willingly enter recovery.

Meanwhile, Clint pondered Micah's newfound patience. If Micah could become a more patient man, maybe Clint could as well.

Silently, Clint closed his eyes and said to himself, "Help me to become a more patient man."

CHAPTER 2: TOLERANCE

"Your beliefs don't make you a better person.
Your behavior does."
~ Sukhrej S. Dillon

One hundred fifty years ago, Slim Hanson and Jim Faucett started the ranch—hence the name, H&F. The cattle operation has always been successful, but the real money made on the ranch today comes from the thirty oil wells that dot the landscape and also from the wild game ranch and the guest ranch. The whole ranch complex continues to be run by the descendants of Hanson and Faucett. Oil money allows the ranch owners to pay better wages to the hands, making a job on the H&F highly coveted and a badge of honor.

Work on the ranch consists of moving cattle from pasture to pasture, branding calves, vaccinating cattle and putting in ear tags, and building and mending fence. Twenty water wells are on the property. They always need attention. Working on irrigation systems is a high priority to make sure all parts of the ranch have access to water.

Ranch hands have to know how to work hard and not

complain. They must be able to lift at least one hundred pounds and be able to stay in the saddle for up to ten hours a day. They have to be willing to do anything that is required and must be one quarter veterinarian, one quarter mechanic, one quarter feed man, and one quarter babysitter. Oh yes, and they have to be completely tech savvy, so they can capture all of the data about the ranch on computer.

Calving takes place in March and April. Hands have to put out hay for them and check the calves regularly. Year round, they have to move the cattle from one pasture to another to prevent them from over-grazing. Rotating cattle also helps fertilize fields and gives them fresh grass to graze.

With more than seventy thousand acres, the H&F is the largest ranch around Bandera and one of the largest in Texas. It stretches from south of Bandera to just north of Hondo and is about twenty-five miles from end to end. Elevation changes from 1,200 to 2,300 feet above sea level throughout the ranch.

The south end of the ranch is near Hondo, the seat of Medina County. The Hondo Creek cuts through that part, providing water for the cattle and also filling several small lakes. There is a bunkhouse near the Hondo end of the ranch that is used when operations shift to that area. Typically, it will have only two or three hands staying there at

a time.

The ranch also has several thousand acres set off and fenced for corralling in native Texas game as well as imported exotic game. The imported elk and American bison (though only outsiders call them anything but buffalo) and hundreds of native white tail deer call the ranch home.

In addition, there are numerous other exotic species including axis, blackbuck, red stag, yak, eland, water buffalo, wildebeests, as well as at least a dozen other species. Hunters pay for their room and board at the hotel that is part of the game ranch, hunting fees, and then another very substantial fee associated with the game they wish to hunt. Hunting fees range from three thousand dollars at the low end to six and seven thousand for many of the species imported from Africa. The highest fee is for the African antelope called a kudu. Each year several hunters gladly fork over more than eighteen thousand dollars to take home a trophy kudu.

The entrance to the game ranch is about ten miles south of the main ranch headquarters so the cowboys and cattle operation is well away from the hunters and the game ranch. The hotel on the game ranch rivals any five-star resort and it stays booked year-round. The hotel lobby has a soaring ceiling with exposed beams. The rock walls are decorated with dozens of big game trophies. A massive western

chandelier hangs in the center of the room, just above a nearly life-sized bronze of a cowboy petting his horse.

A growing number of guests on the game ranch are opting to take wild game tours and shooting the animals only with a camera. Those guests are treated to close up encounters with a number of other species that are not hunted including giraffes, ostriches, zebras, and lions. A unique feature of the game ranch is that guests can choose to hunt by horseback

The H&F also has about one thousand acres set aside as a dude ranch, though they prefer to call it a guest ranch in their marketing materials. In 1941, the H&F owners' grandmother got the idea to start the dude ranch. Early on, most of the guests were servicemen on leave from newly built Lackland Air Force Base, which is less than fifty miles away. Before long, people were coming from all over the world to enjoy a ranch weekend. What makes the H&F Ranch unique among the many other dude ranches in the area is that it is the only one that is also a real working cattle ranch.

The ranch headquarter buildings are located at the north end of the ranch, a few miles south of Bandera. There is a large house that was built in 1870 as the original residence of the owners. Now the ranch foreman and his family live

upstairs and the bottom floor is used as the base for the guest ranch, which includes an office, a gift store, and a saloon that is open in the evenings. There are seventy guest cabins each with two bedrooms and a shared common living area. In addition, there are five barns (for hay, horses, equipment, and two for other supplies) and a horse corral. The Medina River runs through the ranch and makes a horseshoe around the guest ranch portion. At one end of the guest ranch lies Deadwood, a group of building façades that looks like a town from the old west. The evening meal is often served there, as is a cowboy breakfast. Guests can get there either on horseback or they ride out on a hay wagon.

Some of the cabins have wood burning fireplaces. All the furniture is rustic, western, and made of heavy wood. Art decorating the cabin walls includes prints by notable western artists. In the dude ranch headquarters, there are some original oil paintings of scenes out of the old west as well as several bronzes of cowboys and horses frozen in a moment of action. The cabins are named for characters out of the old west. There's Butch Cassidy and next door the Sundance Kid. Other cabin names include Roy Rogers, Wyatt Earp, Judge Roy Bean, Wild Bill Hickok, Doc Holliday, Buffalo Bill, and many others.

Sometimes city people come to the dude ranch and seem to be expecting something similar to a resort setting. As one teenaged girl told her father, "Club Med, it ain't." Accommodations are rustic in keeping with the theme of the ranch. Beds are comfortable; linens are clean; food is first class and plentiful—and all guests get the opportunity to participate in multiple horseback rides as well as a variety of other daily activities. There is swimming in the Olympic sized pool, fishing and tubing on the Medina River, as well as various recreational pursuits including tennis, volleyball, basketball, and horseshoes, to name only a few.

Families typically pay good money to ride horses several times (one of those times to a cowboy breakfast cooked on a chuck wagon in the woods), learning to rope—and the cowboys would always applaud and say they were "natural" cowhands—and practice a bit of line dancing.

In the evening, local entertainers are brought in including musicians, trick ropers, bullwhip instructors, storytellers, and cowboy poets.

The ranch has a nice playground, and a large picnic area. Each evening a bonfire is lit. On a table nearby, there is a supply of clever telescoping forks for roasting marshmallows. Along with the marshmallows there are the requisite graham crackers and chocolate bars for making

s'mores. Occasionally some of the cowboys will join the circle at the bonfire and play a guitar or harmonica.

Jesse James—no kin to the outlaw—is permanently assigned to the guest ranch. Just shy of sixty, he's too old to keep up with the younger hands that take care of the cow, calf operation. He remains one of the most popular employees on the H&F. Years before, his late father had been the general foreman so Jesse grew up on the ranch.

There's always a hint of mischief in Jesse's eyes. He loves a good joke and to make people laugh. He has a set of dentures with the upper plate completely overlaid in gold. The gold teeth are cut out so that white shows through, with the letters T E X A S spelled out. It was widely assumed by guests that Jesse was very proud of his home state. As it turns out, he is a rabid University of Texas Longhorns fan. To end the confusion and announce his school pride, he had his dentist add two silhouettes of the UT longhorn, one before the T and one after the S. Jesse smiles a lot, showing the amazed guests his teeth.

People come to the ranch from all over the world. Two girls from France who came to the States working as au pairs in Connecticut took two weeks and went south for a vacation. They spent two days in New Orleans, then to Austin and San Antonio for a couple of days each. Finally,

they made it to the H&F for the rest of their vacation on an "authentic" ranch that was, in their words, in the "old west." Absolutely giddy at the thought of riding horses for the first time, they arranged for a private ride with Jesse. At lunch that first day, Jesse kept his head down while eating but then lifted his eyes to the girls and said, "We're going to have a good time." One of the other hands laughed and said, "When he says that, look out. He is gettin' ready to pull a joke on you." It was obvious this was an inside joke with some of the conversation being lost in translation.

"I'll try my best to come back with both of you. On my last ride out, I had four. Only came back with two. Maybe we can find 'em this afternoon on our ride."

Jesse dropped his eyes and continued eating. Both girls had a look of alarm on their faces. Other hands at the table laughed and told them he was only kidding, and they would have a good time. While the corners of their mouths turned up a bit, it was obvious they were still a bit concerned.

After quickly finishing their meal, the girls whispered back and forth to each other. Then with a quick glance toward Jesse, they quietly excused themselves and told the reservation desk they changed their minds and wouldn't be riding after all.

In spite of repeated assurances that the ride was safe,

and everyone always came back, they still opted not to ride. Instead they said they would be content to go on the hayride at the end of the day.

Much like a cruise ship, guests are greeted with a flyer under their door each morning with a list of activities for the day. Coffee and juice are waiting in the headquarters building for the early risers, along with fresh newspapers. For those who want it, Jesse and his helpers go from cabin to cabin about an hour before breakfast, ring a dinner triangle, and holler, "Coffee juice! Coffee juice!" Slowly guests emerge from their cabins and are greeted by Jesse's big smile, a hot cup of coffee and a glass of fresh squeezed orange juice. The guests always call him "Coffee Juice" instead of Jesse.

The dining hall will hold 300 plus. Since the starting of the dude ranch operation, the original long tables have been replaced with what looks like oval tables that are cut flat on one end. They are cleverly painted to look like giant horseshoes. The ranch hands eat breakfast before sun up and the guests from the dude ranch eat later either in the dining hall or have the cowboy breakfast in Deadwood. Lunchtime brings the ranch hands and guests together. The cowboys are pretty good at mixing with the guests and the guests love it. As people gather for a meal, there is a

constant jingle from the rowels on the cowboys' spurs.

The centerpiece for each table is a condiment tray with two types of hot sauce, salt and pepper. No linen napkins here. A paper towel roll sits nearby on a colorful bandana. In town at cafes, cowboys will routinely wear their hats during a meal. But on the H&F, no hats are allowed during meals. The rims of the plates are covered with depictions of branding irons. Meal times are noisy. The sound of cutlery, plates, and happy conversation keep the noise level high. In the background are the sounds of classic country and western songs played from a vintage jukebox.

As with all meals on the ranch, breakfast is served family style. Food is on the table, but no one eats until all are seated and the general foreman says grace. The ranch owners are not stingy with grub. They believe ranch work requires a hardy meal for a good day's work. A big breakfast is served to all the hands that want it—and most do. The meal starts promptly at 5:30 followed by a meeting where the general foreman hands out job assignments. Those who are already in the middle of a job quietly slip out and get to work.

Adjoining the dining hall is a large multipurpose room used for guests to relax, read, and play games. Known as The Lodge, there are multiple seating clusters, tables for

board games, and a couple of upright pianos with polite signs that ask they not be played. Above the limestone fireplace is a replica of the H&F brand. Adorning the other walls are multiple items from the old west including antique bridles and other horse tack, historic maps showing the state as it existed a century and a half before, and various western artifacts. Furniture is a combination of wood and leather. Southwestern fabrics are used on throws and pillows.

Six fancy saddles sit on stands scattered throughout The Lodge. They are studded with silver medallions. The story goes that they were made for the original owners of the ranch and have only been used in parades and other special events.

Just down the hill from the dining hall is a large pavilion used for numerous activities including hoedowns, and various cowboy demonstrations like bullwhip lessons, roping lessons, trick roping exhibitions, and line dance lessons.

Wild turkeys and peacocks greet the guests. There is also a large herd of white tail and axis deer that freely roam the grounds of the dude ranch. An ancient stone fence serves as the corral. Adjacent to it is a bunkhouse for the wranglers who are on duty. It is the wranglers' job to take care of the two hundred horses on the ranch, including the fifty plus horses used exclusively by ranch guests.

Each morning the wranglers use a pickup or a Jeep to round up the number of horses needed for that day. They honk the horn a few times as they drive through the pasture. The horses have been conditioned by years of the same routine morning after morning and come toward the corral without resistance.

Work on the H&F is unrelenting, lasting from dawn to dusk. There are no union breaks. No holidays other than Christmas day.

Most of the hands live in or near town, which is about a mile from the ranch. Five hands are required to live on the ranch in rotation. They live in the bunkhouse for a week and must be on-call, in case the sheriff calls to say there are cattle on the road, or there is some other emergency with the cattle.

Hands work rotating assignments among the three parts of the ranch: the working ranch, wild game ranch, and guest ranch. This work rotation broadens their experience and provides greater variety to their work. Their broad experience makes them especially valuable when, for example, the guest ranch is packed to overflowing—like at Spring Break and in summer—or the wild game ranch is drowning in hunters during the first two weeks of deer season. A few hands, like Jesse, are permanently assigned to

one part of the ranch.

Because of the size of the ranch, hands often stay in line shacks for several days and up to a week or longer while working on the back on the ranch. It just doesn't make sense to take up work time to travel the twenty-five miles from the south end to the bunkhouse. There are few roads on the ranch but there are plenty of cow and horse trails. Some of the work these days is done on four-wheelers, but the seasoned hands still prefer a horse to a motor-driven mount.

This week, Micah has a crew of sixteen other men—most of them new hires.

They spent the week moving cattle from pasture to pasture. Many of the pastures are miles apart, requiring a cattle drive that will occupy most of the day. Even though all the hands grew up riding horses, long days are spent primarily sitting on a horse and are particularly grueling. Most of the crew are in their 20s. Micah knew the young crew would require about as much guidance as the cattle. Long days of moving cattle means no breaks and no lunch—only the jerky they carry in their saddlebags.

Clint couldn't believe how green the young hands are. While they're all experienced horsemen, they don't seem to know much about cattle. As they move the cattle, Clint has to continually correct them. It looks to him like they learned

to move cattle watching Rawhide on TV. He has to keep telling them to quit scaring the cattle—stop their poking and prodding and just lead them. They don't have to so much drive the cattle as to simply show the cattle where they need to go.

Suddenly the cattle got spooked and started running in the opposite direction. The young cowboys didn't know what to do other than holler and wave their hats like they had seen done in cowboy movies. Clint yelled at several of the hands and told them how to gently get behind the cattle and regain control. He couldn't believe these hands were actually getting paid to work with cattle. It was as though some of them had never been around any cows before.

One of the young hands smarted off to Clint and told him he was not the boss. Clint got off his horse and said, "If you don't like takin' direction from me, get off your horse and do somethin' about it!" Clint bowed up his chest and doubled up his fists. Wisely, the young man rode on, and he also kept clear of Clint. He had already heard about Clint's hair trigger and now he'd experienced it. He didn't want to find out if Clint was as good with his fists as the other hands had said.

By noon, Clint had had enough. He told Micah he didn't think any of them belonged on the ranch and he wished

Micah would ask the foreman to fire them.

"They're just boys," Micah said. "We used to cut up like that when we were their age."

Clint said they may have been a bit rowdy when they were younger, but they always did their work well and they didn't have to be corrected like these young hands.

"Just watch 'em. They're getting' the hang of it." Micah continued, "Besides I know they need their jobs. I think they'll all turn out to be top hands."

How can Micah tolerate the near insubordination of these overgrown boys? Correcting them doesn't seem to have much of an impact. Why doesn't Micah take a harder line with them the way he has seen him do so many times in the past? What has gotten into him? It was like Micah was a different person.

Clint pondered the easy-going manner of Micah. Was he right about these young men? Do they have what it takes to become top ranch hands? Clint wasn't so sure, but he respected Micah, so he determined he would make it a point to ease up on them. He'll try not being as demanding of the new hands, and he'll try to hold his tongue if and when one of them slips up again.

Clint saw Micah being tolerant in other areas. If a meal was not on time or if it was not as hot as he liked, he didn't

have a tirade at the cook but would take it in stride. In the past, wranglers and stable hands who didn't have his horse ready on time, would have been the recipient of his bad temper. But now it was as if Micah had the tolerance of a man who was much older and wiser.

Micah knew Clint was right the young men were not catching on to ranch life as quickly as he hoped, but he also knew if he could exercise tolerance with them, they would come along. He smiled to himself and thought about how hard he used to be on new hires. Frequently, he would succeed in having men quit before they had worked an entire week. But his whole outlook on life in general, and his job in particular, had changed since entering recovery. When he was drinking, he would take only so much before he would put a man in his place. He wouldn't take any sass and he wouldn't tell a hand twice how to do his job. If he couldn't do it the way it was supposed to be done, he would tell him he would find someone who could.

To Clint, this week seemed like it would never end. The days were hot and never-ending. Since it was mid-August, they had daylight until after 8:00 pm. And all ranch hands knew that the job was a sun up to sun down job. It was not unheard of for them to work 15-16 hours each day.

By the time the week was over, they had moved more

than 2,500 head of cattle. Clint was physically tired, but he was also exhausted from having to help rein in the young crew. But Micah seemed to have an almost super human ability to tolerate whatever came his way.

Micah was sure his tolerance of others was a result of his recovery. When he first stopped drinking, Micah felt if he could just stay sober, he would be doing all he needed for recovery. But as he worked the Steps of Recovery, he realized there were many areas of his life that needed to change.

Becoming more tolerant was high on the list of changes he wanted to make in himself. To his surprise, the more he cultivated tolerance, the easier it was for him to be more tolerant.

Riding home with Micah on Friday evening, Clint remembered how in years past, he and Micah would go to the Cheer Up Saloon together and have a few beers to blow off the pressure of the week. He knew Micah would not go with him since he had stopped drinking. But Clint wondered how Micah was able to put up with the inexperienced hands without having several drinks.

Clint wanted what Micah had. How could he make the same changes in his life? Clint silently bowed his head and said, "Help me to become more tolerant."

Chapter 3: Gentleness

"If you don't know where you are going,
it would be a good idea not to use your spurs."
~ Western wisdom

Clint's lawyer was successful at continuing to delay his inevitable day in court. Through shrewd legal maneuvering, he told Clint the longer they waited for trial, the better. He also told Clint he had an opportunity to show he was a changed man. It was essential that Clint not get into any more trouble. That was easy, Clint thought, since the only real trouble he had ever had with the law was driving under the influence, if he didn't count the many times he had been arrested for being drunk and disorderly or for public intoxication. Most of the time he had only been in jail overnight while he sobered up.

For most of the previous twenty years, Clint has been a fixture at the Cheer Up. From the outside, the Cheer Up gives the appearance of a very small bar. There are a few tables, a short bar area. Hanging from the ceiling are hundreds of bras. Each is signed and dated. No story. The decorations are simply left to the imagination of the person

viewing or the memory of the one involved in labeling and hanging the unusual decorations.

On one side of the room is a door that leads to another part of the bar. In that room are more tables. Then through the next door there is a room open to the street with more tables and bar stools. The real surprise comes out the back door. There is a large semi-open space with multiple stages, a barbecue area, a large full-service bar, and several buildings surrounding the area, which sells beer and various food items. There are tables and bar stools for several hundred and a dance floor for a couple of hundred more. This is surprising, given the population of the city was less than one thousand.

The bar stools in the outdoor performance area are homemade. They have a horseshoe welded to the single stalk frame that serves as a footrest. These are set in concrete around a serpentine bar that winds its way through the large patio. Off to the side are several kettle barbecue pits that measure about four feet across. One night a week is steak night when customers are invited to bring their own meat and cook while enjoying the music.

There are special "hunter's weekends" in November to cater to the many city folks who escape to the Hill Country to practice their marksmanship. Trees in the outdoor bar

area are permanently covered in Christmas twinkle lights giving the whole area a festive atmosphere. The men's room has no toilet seats. Apparently, the management got tired of cleaning them. Outside on one wall of the bar are an uncountable number of license plates from various states including a number from Canada.

Directly across the street from the Cheer Up is the Stumble Inn. Once there was an actual inn by that name but over the years, only the saloon attached to it survived. The Stumble Inn is as busy as the Cheer Up on most nights. Both bars have live music several nights a week. On any given night, customers will usually walk back and forth between the two bars, as though they might miss something if they don't go to both. Each evening, the Marshal's office will have an officer patrol the street between the two bars to make sure no one takes a beer from one bar to the other—a clear violation of the rules of the liquor control board in Texas. They will also try to spot the cowboys who have drunk too much and forcefully encourage them to call for a taxi. More than once, the local police have called dispatch to have them send a cab. On Friday and Saturday nights, there is an unofficial cab stand by the curb between the two bars with at least a couple of cabs waiting to be pressed into service.

Clint would go to the Stumble Inn occasionally, but he felt more at home at the Cheer Up. Most evenings, Clint was in the habit of eating dinner with his wife and then heading to the Cheer Up, where he would stay until midnight. On weekends, he would stay until the bar closed at two a.m.

Clint has his own stool at the Cheer Up. It is at the far end of the bar, away from the door. And if someone is already sitting there, he will hang around until the bartender or barmaid asks him or her to move. Locals know better than to sit there.

He had already skinned his knuckles more than once defending his territory. Admittedly most of those times had happened years earlier when Clint had been the local rodeo star. He rode bulls and broncs and was the best roper in the county. But even after his rodeo prime, people still gave him his due and left the end stool vacant just in case he came for a beer—more than likely six to ten of them.

One of the reasons he liked that stool was because there was an eight by ten glossy of him behind the bar, right in front of his stool. He had still been in high school when the shot was taken. It showed him high on the shoulders of a massive bull, left hand buried in the rigging and his right hand high in the air. The bull was well known in those days for never having been ridden to the buzzer, until Clint's ride.

The bull went unto a clockwise spin and immediately reversed to spin the other way. All other cowboys had not made it out of the well of the first turn, much else lasted for the change of direction. Clint not only stayed in his seat, but he continued with his right hand high in the air several seconds after the buzzer. Then in a moment of vanity, lifted his hat high for the crowd and gently slid down the left side of the bull. The crowd went wild. That story was such a legend that it was embellished and retold at least once a week. And when there was a newcomer present, and Clint was on his bar throne, the story was usually so exaggerated that it took a full fifteen minutes to tell it. Meanwhile Clint would just smile slightly and chug his beer.

While in his early twenties that photo and the accompanying stories brought in enough business the bartender would often let Clint drink for free. Even into his late twenties they would still spot Clint his first two beers until they started making him pay. Now the only thing left of his glory days is the faded photo behind the bar and his unofficial but mostly permanent claim to the end stool.

Several pool tables were adjacent to the bar. Each had a light with a rectangular shade hanging low over the table, providing islands of light in an otherwise dark room. When someone was taking his turn shooting, leaning down to the

table spotlighted him for a few seconds. With each shot, the balls would crack and the only thing remaining in the spotlight would be the green felt table.

In larger cities, pool tables took dollar bills or took credit cards. But at the Cheer Up, the tables still took quarters. The challenging player would lay his quarter on the bank above the coin slot signifying the next game was taken. Sometimes there would be a short line of quarters ready to challenge the winner of the previous game.

Barroom pool games are typically not a game of skill and finesse. They are generally about breaking as hard as possible and then showing off some fancy cue ball dancing as they make shots in rapid succession until they missed. And when they miss, that's time to pick up their bottle of beer and drink half in four or five huge swallows.

Ceremoniously the players chalked their sticks between every shot and walked rapidly around the table looking for the best shot. Then they lined up the cue ball and their target, taking three or four pumps before letting their stick fly forward much harder than needed but producing a satisfying series of crashes as the balls collide.

This is not pool hall billiards. This is the down-and-dirty barroom game of Eight Ball played on little tables that are seldom level. Cue sticks are worn, like the cushions on the

tables. Nobody seems to care about the condition of the equipment, but many complain anyway. Especially when they lose. It is always the "damned crooked cue stick" or the "damned spongy cushions" or the "damned table that was not level." Never is a game lost because of being outplayed or on account of hitting the balls too hard. But that is barroom pool.

Three big screen TVs show the current games for whichever sport is in season. The sound is down so the jukebox could be heard. The only people watching are cowboys who come in by themselves and are not looking to pick up one of the local sweet things that frequent the bar late into the night. Clint thought to himself how he would think of the young women as sweet things and the older women as bar flies. Usually one of the TVs would be tuned to a rodeo event. A few satellite channels carried bull riding and other rodeo events throughout the evening. To the uninitiated, it is not clear where the events were taking place or why anyone would want to endlessly watch them.

Clint had picked up younger women and older women here. He didn't discriminate much. Once he had drunk three or four beers, it was his habit to start looking for someone to spend a couple of hours with him in a room at the Better Days. He would tell jokes, laughing aloud whether anyone

else laughed or not. People were typically drawn to Clint, and most genuinely liked him early in the evening. After several beers, however, he became louder and more obnoxious. Unaccompanied women were always his target.

He was not looking for love. Just looking for a romp that would drive away the loneliness for the evening. At least that's what he told himself. What he couldn't answer was why he had the same behavior before his wife kicked him out. He still would pick up women and take them to the Better Days motel before going home and getting in bed next to his wife. All he could think of that made sense for him was his wife didn't really understand him, and he found her a bit frigid. Yes, that's what she was. She was frigid. Why couldn't she take an interest in him the way the women at the Cheer Up did? She used to laugh at his jokes, but the laughing stopped several years ago.

His idea of foreplay with his wife was to say, "Brace yourself." So what! He could never understand why his wife was not as ready to be sexual as the flavor of the evening was when he shared a bed with his latest conquest. They didn't expect romance. They knew the score. They were there for a quick flip in the hay and then hearing Clint say, "That was so nice. I'll call you in a few days and we will do it again, huh?"

Sometimes he called. Often, he didn't. But either way his casual partners always seemed to believe they were something special because the great Clint Hazard had given them some of his attention and a bit of lovin' for the evening. He long since stopped looking for Miss Right and settled for Miss Right Now. Often in the morning he would wake up with no memory of the night before or who was in bed with him. But he always congratulated himself on being such a stud and thought of himself as "The Man."

Clint was great in bed, he told himself. His wife used to think so. And he had plenty of satisfied fillies that seemed to enjoy his company. He fancied himself a real Lothario. He felt he was doing women a favor when he picked them out to be the object of his attention for the evening.

After ten o'clock in the bar, there would usually be a cowboy or two who had laid his head on the table or the bar and was snoring, waiting to be asked to leave. By then, most of the single ladies had left the bar. The few who were left became the focus of Clint's attention. He was usually ahead of most of them by several beers. As the old adage goes, the later it got, the better they looked. He was usually successful in getting someone to leave with him. After all, he was good looking, and popular around town.

One of the waitresses was old enough to be Clint's

mother. The cowboys always joked with Dottie as she served them round after round. They all knew her story and how she had worked there for more than forty years. She had waited for her cowboy to come in and kiss her and take her away from the Cheer Up. That fantasy ended twenty years before.

One of his friends bet Clint that he wouldn't kiss Dottie. At that point it was anyone's guess as to how much Clint had had to drink. All he knew was that for the four hours he had been there he had been to the urinal at least a dozen times. So, figuring one trip equaled one beer means he had put away a lot.

He loudly accepted the bet and Dottie came and sat on his lap and he gave her a deep kiss to the hoots and hollers of his peers. For Dottie, it was as if her prince of a cowboy had come riding in, but suddenly, she realized, he was not just young; he was the age of her youngest son. She turned away in horror telling herself she was going to quit the Cheer Up tonight. Like all her promises to herself, she discarded it before the evening was out.

One of his fellow boozehounds said, "Clint, I think you're in heat. And you seem to stay that way." Those close by laughed but Clint either didn't hear the comment or acted as though he didn't.

Soon the bartender sounded out Last Call and Clint, as was his practice, ordered two more brews. Quickly downing the first, he started on the second. He thought about how empty his room was at the Better Days. He went over to Dottie and whispered in her ear, "I want you to come to my room tonight. I will make you so very happy."

"Oh honey, I think you are as sexy as hell, but I can't."

"Why not?"

"Because I have to live with myself in the mornin'."

He didn't understand or even care about her response. He quickly forgot the encounter and went one by one to the remaining waitresses making indecent propositions to each. Laughing behind his back, Clint was oblivious to their ridicule and scorn. He just called for his taxi and made it back to his new home at the Better Days. Collapsing into bed with his clothes on, he slept the sleep of the deeply addicted. Snoring before he hit the pillow, Clint ended the night in a fog that would continue into the next day. Even as his friends would rib him about his behavior with Dottie, he wouldn't remember any of it.

That night, Clint hit a new low. He wet his bed. When he woke up in the morning, his mattress was completely soaked. How had he dropped to this? When he got home the next day, there was a terse note from the motel manager

saying he had to pay for a new mattress by the next day or he would be evicted. Then the words, "And you know why!!!"

Attached was a bill for two hundred dollars. More money he didn't have. But he couldn't lose his room, so he started digging and came up with the money necessary to keep from being turned out of the cheapest room in town. To make matters worse, the motel clerk would no longer look him in the eye.

How could his life have gotten so off track? When had just having a bit of fun and kicking up his heels become something that was taking his life down the gutter? Clint told himself he had to turn over a new leaf. He recognized drinking was the problem. Right then and there, he decided to cut back and not drink as often or as much as he normally did. He figured that would be a way to save money too, so he could buy another pickup if he ever got his license back. And, oh yes, he needed to put back some money to pay his lawyer when he finally did go to trial. It also didn't help that he had to take a taxi everywhere he went, except to work. As time went on, he became proud of himself for curtailing a lot of his partying. Instead of going to the Cheer Up every night, he was only going once or twice during the week and on weekends. On the nights he

didn't go to the Cheer Up, he stayed in his room and drank beer and ate potato chips for dinner. The little fridge in his room was crowded with beer, not leaving room for any food.

Clint felt he had become friends with Josh, the taxi driver he used the most. He actually bragged to his drinking buddies it was as if he had his own chauffeur. However, it rankled the driver that not once had Clint left a tip or in any way treated him other than as hired help. Josh glared at him through the rearview mirror when Clint was recounting some story he told at the bar. It didn't help the relationship any when Clint threw up in the back seat of the cab on the way from the Cheer Up to his motel.

"That's it! You can get someone else to drive you around town. I'll never let your cheap ass in my car again. And good luck finding another cabby. When I'm through tellin' 'em about you, you won't get anyone to pick you up."

The driver was right. Clint was not able to get any taxi to pick him up. Even though there were three cab companies in town, Clint guessed they all knew each other. "What do I care?" Clint said to himself. There was a café, a grocery store, and a liquor store within walking distance from his motel. The fridge at the motel would hold almost a half case of beer. He could have his own parties in his

room. And on nights when he wanted to be around people, he reasoned he could walk to the Cheer Up. It was only about two miles from his motel room.

Throughout autumn, Clint continued riding to work with Micah. Even though they worked together every day, Clint wondered why their friendship seemed to be getting more distant. Every morning at five, Micah picked him up. Each evening just after dark, Micah delivered him to his motel.

Clint tried to engage Micah with stories of his most recent romantic conquests and of his legendary ability to drink more than others. Micah would listen and nod his head, but it was more of an "I heard you" nod than an "I think that's cool" nod. Clint had a hard time figuring how Micah could have changed so much that he didn't even want to party anymore. After all, they had been partying together since high school.

The last time Clint invited Micah to go to the Cheer Up with him, Micah said, "Clint, I just don't go there anymore. That life was never good for me. I knew if I didn't make some changes I would lose my wife and I wasn't going to risk that. Besides, I have some other interests now that are taking up several evenings a week."

"Really? Doing what?"

"Oh, just some guys I get together with. Nothin' big. Just sittin' around talkin'," said Micah.

Clint didn't know what to make of that. Micah didn't tell him any more. He suspected Micah might have been going to church except he knew the meetings were in the evenings. Clint wondered whether he might have joined the lodge but that didn't sound like Micah either. *I wonder where he is going*, Clint thought to himself.

****

With winter over, duties at the ranch began to shift. Part of every week included hauling hay from one pasture to another. There was just not enough grass to sustain the cattle. They also still had to move cattle from pasture to pasture to keep what grass was still growing from getting too trampled down.

The big shift in late winter was getting ready for calving season. The foreman had carefully timed breeding so that all the calves would drop before the end of April. Although most births went smoothly, a considerable number of calves had to be helped into the world. This was especially true for the heifers. Without any experience giving birth, they would sometimes get in the thicket where they couldn't be seen or

get separated from the rest of the herd.

The hands were in the pastures each day keeping careful track of all cows that were ready to calve. The H&F has upwards of five thousand calves each year. It is crucial that every birth is monitored and every calf is accounted for.

Micah was in charge of eight of the twenty-five management units on the ranch. He depended on Clint to be on top of everything Micah couldn't do himself. Clint thrived on the extra work that came at calving time. But he also partly dreaded this time of year because he knew Micah was stretched pretty thin. In the past Micah would push the men hard and take out his frustrations on them when they were shorthanded. Micah was known as the toughest of the tough. He worked harder and longer than most other hands except for Clint. Clint could stay with him and give just as good of a day's work.

The first hint Clint had that this was going to be a different calving season was when Micah picked him up that March morning with a smile on his face. "You know what today is, don't you?" asked Micah.

"Monday, right?"

"Yes, it's Monday. But do you know what Monday?"

"I give up. What Monday is it?"

"It is the beginning of calvin' season," replied Micah.

"Beginnin' this week, most of the hands will be living in the bunkhouse until early April. You ready?"

"Of course. But why are you smilin'?" asked Clint. "You always dread calvin' season."

"Oh, I've been thinkin' this is one of the most special times of the year. We get to help bring new life into the world."

Clint thought Micah was going soft. He had never talked like that before. Cows, calves, hay hauling—it had all just seemed like work in the past and Micah hadn't shown any preference over one ranch job to another.

Over the next three weeks, Micah and Clint worked side-by-side most of the time. Several times a day, Clint would catch a bit of a smile on Micah's face. Just an upturn to one side of his mouth, or there would be a glint in his eye, as though his eyes were smiling.

Together, they assisted in more than a hundred births. Most days, their shirts and jeans were covered in blood and mucus. It was not like the old days. Now cleanliness was important for the future fertility of the cows, so Micah and Clint were forever washing their hands and cleaning their equipment.

Clint watched Micah and the gentle way he treated each cow and calf. He would talk to the cows, soothing them with

his voice. Even though the act of helping a calf into the world took strength and lots of physical labor, Micah was as gentle as he could be with each animal.

There was no dinner bell in the evening during calving season. Hands who had overnight duty worked until last light and then headed for the corral. They knew all they had to do was dismount and wash their hands. The stable hands always took care of curry combing and feeding each horse. Not having to care for their own mount was a luxury only afforded to hands on the H&F. Other ranches required each hand to take care to feed and water their horse, brush and curry comb them, and then eat. What the H&F owners had learned years earlier was they got more out of the hands by taking that chore from then and providing them a generous meal and a soft cot. They then went to bed early and were ready for another day when 4:30 am came.

In the bunkhouse each evening, Micah still wore the same half grin. While all the hands were exhausted, and many were short-tempered, Micah acted as though he was rested and relaxed. He spoke softly to the other hands. It was amazing to watch how his gentle manner and speech rubbed off on the other hands.

What has happened to my friend? thought Clint. What accounted for the changes he had seen in one of the H&F's

toughest cowboys? Micah still worked as hard as or harder than anyone. He still brooked no nonsense or slacking off from any of the hands. But Micah had definitely changed. His gruff exterior was gone. His words and demeanor were softer.

The big surprise for Clint was how it seemed like the respect the hands had for Micah was growing. They always looked up to him but now they enjoyed just being around Micah. At mealtime, the men tended to try to sit near him. In the bunkhouse, there was always someone hanging around Micah wanting to get his opinion on something or just chewing the fat with him.

Clint found his regard for Micah increasing as well. The new qualities he saw in Micah were much more appealing than the tough exterior cultivated by many men. Clint had a new respect for his oldest friend. He longed to be able to command the esteem of other men—not for his drinking exploits or his carousing around. But for deeper, core-level character qualities that were now so apparent in Micah.

That night just before Clint got into his bunk, he bowed his head and said, "I want to be marked by gentleness. Help me to become a gentle man." He drifted off to sleep thinking about the many changes he needed to make in his life.

CHAPTER 4: KINDNESS

"You will never reach your destination if you stop and throw stones, at every dog that barks."
~ Winston Churchill

Calving season done, there was much to do on the ranch. Haying and maintaining the water wells consumed most of their time. The month had come and gone without Clint much noticing. He called his wife, but she hung up on him. Each time he saw Tripp at work, his son treated him like he was a stranger or worse.

Lost in thought, Clint went about his work, trying to give his best, hoping he would somehow be able to become a better man like Micah. Many of the days passed quickly with little time to think about anything before he heard the dining hall bell. Lunch gobbled down, it was back to work until dusk.

But this day, time seemed to drag. Clint kept thinking of his childhood and how tough things had been back then. He remembered thinking how he vowed his life was going to turn out differently.

Clint lost his innocence when he was just a child. He

had seen vile things happen at the hands of his father. How could a man beat his children and abuse his wife? What would possess a man to take a whip to a six-year-old boy for breaking a plate? The scars on his back and his thighs reminded him of the first time he thought his father was a mad man. What could cause a man to do such things to his family?

Clint knew he had to escape. But he also needed to protect his sister and his mother. One day, he found his father's secret bottle in the garage. The rest of his supply of whiskey was in the house but he would come out each evening to have a slug or two, so no one would know how much he really drank. But Clint knew. And Clint discovered he could also find relief with just a couple of swallows himself.

That began a practice that continued to this day. When times were tough, Clint would take a slug or two out of his bottle and find things didn't seem so bad. In fact, the burning that went down his throat seemed to bring instant relief. For most days after that first drink in the garage, Clint would try to get back to that place of warmth and peace that drinking gave him.

The first long drink was the best. With each subsequent drink, he would try to recreate that warm feeling. But after

several attempts, Clint knew all he got from his efforts was another in a long string of nights where he numbed himself until the next morning when he couldn't remember much of what happened the night before.

Clint listened as Micah told him to saddle up and follow him to the corral. They needed to rebuild the fence that had been kicked down by a startled mare. As they rode, Clint's thoughts went back to his childhood.

He remembered the first time he thought one day he would pay his father back for his cruelty. Someday he would get back at his dad. Then he would be big enough to protect his sister and his mother. The thoughts of his tortured childhood stirred his heart. He remembered the hatred that consumed him back then. He also realized once he had finally escaped to college at age seventeen, he had not been successful at protecting his sister or his mother. His sister married soon after he left home.

His mother was put in the hospital one more time with broken bones. After that she got a restraining order, divorced his father, and moved only God knows where. Clint had not seen nor heard from her in more than twenty years.

This return to his sad childhood only caused him more pain. Why hadn't he done a better job of protecting his

mother and sister? He reminded himself he was just a little boy then but that brought no relief.

On the way home from the ranch, Micah pulled into a convenience store so Clint could pick up a few groceries. Micah waited near the register trying to purchase some gum and a pound of coffee. The young clerk was talking on his cell phone oblivious to the fact that customers were waiting to check out.

The clerk finally got off the phone and the man in line in front of Micah gruffly said, "It's about time! I thought you were gonna talk all night!"

The clerk responded in kind. "It didn't hurt you to wait a few moments! Get off my back!"

When Micah went to the register, he noticed the young man had a big frown on his face. As his purchases were being rung up, Micah said, "Looks like you got some bad news. Are you all right?"

"That was my dad. My mom was crossing the street and got hit by a car. They've taken her to the hospital. I don't know how she is doing."

"Look. I know Zach who owns this store. You go check on your mother and I'll take care of things here until you get back. Don't worry about a thing. Zach will understand. You need to be with your folks."

Clint couldn't believe it! They had worked hard for 15 hours and now they were going to have to stay there until the kid got back from the hospital. Micah caught Clint's sigh and saw his incredulous look.

"Listen Clint," Micah said softly. "It's not far to your motel. You can walk there in about fifteen minutes. Why don't you go on ahead? I'll pick you up in the morning."

"You don't mind? Thanks. I think I'll do that." And Clint walked out the door.

If any other man had been going through the changes Clint saw in Micah, he would have simply believed he was going soft. But Clint knew Micah was still the strong, rugged cowboy he had always known. What he was seeing in Micah was a transformation that started somewhere deep inside. It had been about eighteen months now since the changes started. Clint had thought Micah would surely go back to his old self, but he had been wrong. The partying never started again. Those strange changes in his personality—the softness—seemed to have become permanent.

The most striking change of all was the kindness that seemed to permeate every fiber of Micah's being. As he walked to his motel room, Clint continued to reflect on what he had just witnessed. He walked on, deep in thought.

As he got to the motel driveway, he bit his lip and said,

"I don't know if I can do it, but if possible, I would like to be thought of as a kind person. Help me to become that—somehow—someday.

CHAPTER 5: LOVE

"Any man who would make an x-rated movie
ought to have to take
his daughter to it.
~ John Wayne

Clint liked to think of himself as a lover. If there was one thing he was good at it was loving. He had long since lost count of his sexual conquests. When he still had his pickup, there were few weeks when he wasn't in somebody's panties—usually more than one. He was sure the other hands looked up at him for his virility.

He used to be embarrassed the next morning when he couldn't remember the name of the person in the bed next to him. Now he just habitually said, "Wow, I must have had a wonderful night! What's your name?" Sometimes his bedmate would be angry. But most of the time, the women were as hung over as he was and didn't feel anything more than a headache and a sick stomach. They didn't have any illusions their connection the night before had any bearing on their future.

Clint liked to think of himself as a man's man—a

cowboy's cowboy. He was as macho as they came. More than once he had gotten into fights with hands who found out he had been messing with their wives. Somehow, he was able to keep his job through each of these skirmishes.

One jealous husband who worked at another ranch showed up at the H&F dining hall one morning a couple of years earlier. He made loud threats to Clint and told him he was there to even the score. The man was huge. He had at least six inches on Clint's lean frame and outweighed Clint by more than fifty pounds. As the man proceeded to destroy the dining hall and wallop Clint again and again, the other hands jumped in and subdued the attacker.

For the first time, Clint realized his dalliances could prove fatal if he crossed the wrong man. He was glad they were not living a century earlier because Clint had no doubt the offended husband would have settled things with a gun.

None of his liaisons lasted long, although a couple looked like they could turn into something. In the end, Clint realized he was less interested in these people because of who they were but rather for how they made him feel or what they could do for him sexually. While he hated to admit it, Clint realized he had been substituting sex for love.

Micah used to run around as much as he did. Why had

he stopped and how had he done it? Clint was determined to ask Micah if he ever got the chance.

Later that day, he and Micah were riding out to a neighboring management area. Clint knew they had about a forty-minute ride, so he decided this was as good of a time as any to ask Micah about the changes in his relationship with his wife.

"So Micah, I've been wonderin' about somethin'. You don't have to talk about it if you don't want to. But we used to go out together with lots of women. Used to, there was never a Friday night we weren't at the Cheer Up dancin' and chasin' skirts. And you used to catch about as many as me. What happened to you? Why'd you change?"

For a while they rode on without Micah saying anything. Clint wasn't sure he had heard his question at first. He was going to ride closer and ask again when Micah finally spoke.

"Do you remember year before last when we were at the Cattleman's Convention in San Anton?"

"Sure," replied Clint. "How could I forget it? We had a great time. And I remember you spendin' most of your time with a beautiful dark-headed girl that had a body that just wouldn't quit."

"Well it all started there." Micah continued, "I was just

havin' fun for a few days but that lady really fell for me. Before I knew it, she was tellin' me she loved me and that she knew we would have a wonderful life together. She even owned her own ranch, nothin' like the H&F but still a respectable spread.

"She took me out to see it and it was amazin'. The main house was built of stone. It was magnificent. She showed me a couple of barns. In addition to her cattle, she had a quarter horse operation that was second to none.

"As she showed me around, I started to realize she was makin' plans for the future that included me. I should have been flattered but instead I was frightened.

"She took me into the back half of the stable. It was finished out with an office but had an adjoinin' room that opened into the most masculine area. There was a huge fireplace—so large I could almost stand up in it. She had a pool table, a full bar, the biggest TV I'd ever seen. The furniture was rustic and manly. It was the kind of place where any man would have felt like a king.

"We sat on the couch and she told me, 'This will be your man cave. After we're married, you can make whatever changes in it you like. I just want you to be comfortable and happy.'

"I was stunned! Sure, we had had some pretty good sex for the past couple of days but I hadn't said anythin' about marriage. I thought she understood. She even commented on my weddin' ring. I was just blowing off steam while we were in the big city. I wasn't looking for another wife or another life. I just wanted to have a good time—a very temporary good time.

"I had to do somethin' to get her out of the thought I was going to be her Mister. I told her the first thing that came to my mind. I said, 'You don't understand. I'm not capable of bein' monogamous.'

"You would have thought I slapped her. She sat back in stunned silence. In a few moments, she began to cry and said, 'Get out! I don't ever want to see you again.'

"If you'll remember, I left the convention that evenin' and came back to the ranch. But on the way back here, I got to thinkin' about what I'd told her, that I wasn't capable of being monogamous. I realized I had spoken the truth. And I didn't like the look I got of myself. That was thc day I determined I had to change. I didn't know how to do it or what all would be involved but I decided that day I would never again be unfaithful to my wife and I would make any changes I needed to in order to be able to change the way I

wanted to be."

Clint rode on in silence, contemplating what Micah had told him. Neither of them spoke again until they finished their ride. They dismounted and took care of the fence that needed repair. The sun was low in the sky, so they saddled up and headed for the corral. Neither said a word for the trip back.

Clint realized he had much to learn about love. Who were the people he truly loved? He knew he loved his wife but realized he had never really shown her that love. He loved his son, but Tripp displayed the same rebellious spirit Clint had when he was a boy. Beyond these, Clint realized he never really loved anyone else. Sure, he knew he loved his mother, but it had been so long since he had seen her he wasn't sure if there was still any love there.

What Clint knew for sure is he didn't love himself. He didn't even like himself most of the time. What was there about him that was loveable anyway? Try as he might, Clint couldn't shake the depression settling in. Usually he was able to cover his feelings of self loathing by drinking, taking some pills, or by picking up someone who wanted companionship for the evening. But today, Clint knew he just needed to be by himself. He needed to contemplate

what Micah had told him.

Many women through the years said they loved him. What he now realized is most of them were as incapable as he was to ever really love someone else. What they loved were the gifts he gave them or the sex they had. But beyond a tumble in the hay, a roll in the sack, none of them were still around after a few weeks. He couldn't blame them.

Clint knew he was a user. And he didn't mean his drug consumption. He used people. He used women for sex, used men to get help with a job, used his family to give him the look of respectability. He even used Micah because he knew he could make his work life easier or more difficult.

Yes, Clint was a user. That was a better description than to think of himself as a lover.

But Micah, on the other hand, was a lover. In spite of his past cheating, he knew Micah was now faithful to his wife. Micah showed a deep abiding care for his wife that went beyond just not cheating on her.

He could see the love in Micah as he spoke to thc hands. It seemed strange to Clint to think of a cowboy loving other cowboys, but he knew that was true of Micah. He even knew Micah loved him. Why else would he put up with his poor attitude and bad behavior over so many years?

Theirs was a friendship based on love—mainly the love Micah had for Clint.

Clint was finally coming to understand love was not a sexual act but was something that came from within a person and was expressed in actions. As midnight approached, Clint once more found himself talking out loud. "I don't know how to become a loving man, but I want to be one. Help me learn the true meaning of love. Help me to love others and to love myself."

With that, Clint turned in and spent the next several hours staring at the ceiling, thinking about his conversation with Micah.

CHAPTER 6: INTEGRITY

"If you always tell the truth, you never have to try and remember what lie you told."
~ Unknown

The last week in April brought another week for Clint and Micah to be on call. Neither minded it so much. They enjoyed having a break in their usual routine. Clint really enjoyed it since it meant he got to sleep in a more comfortable bed at the bunkhouse than the motel provided and because his dinner would be more than beer and chips.

At least two of their on-call days would be spent camping on the trail. They had to go to the southernmost management area and perform routine water well maintenance and check on the stock in that pasture. They would also need to move that herd to a neighboring pasture. It wasn't difficult work, but it would be time consuming with just the two of them to manage the move.

Clint and Micah saddled up right after breakfast and headed south. It would take all day to get where they were going. Along the way they would check the fence lines and

do a rough count of the cattle. The calves were only a few weeks old, so they needed to check on as many as possible as they rode south.

The morning was crisp and cool. They both seemed to enjoy each other's company. Every now and then Micah would break into song. Clint would laugh at him telling him he couldn't sing but Micah would continue anyway. Secretly, Clint wished he could abandon his self-consciousness and do the same. But it wasn't in Clint. Besides, Clint really couldn't sing!

By mid-morning, they noticed buzzards circling overhead. They knew something was dead nearby. They hoped it wasn't one of the calves but feared it was. Directly, they dropped into a shallow ravine and found what the vultures had spotted. A heifer had died giving birth. Sometimes the anatomy of a cow is such that they just can't give birth—at least not without help.

Micah was sad. He felt responsible because he knew they had to be especially mindful of the heifers as they calved the first time. This poor thing should have been moved closer to the front of the ranch where they could have kept watch on her.

This wasn't the first or the last head they would lose

during the year. While most of the cattle did well, there were occasional losses. With more than twenty thousand head to care for, it was inevitable there would be some losses. That didn't make it any easier for Micah to stomach.

They knew nature would take its course. The vultures would pick the carcasses clean within a week. Life would go on for the rest of the herd.

They rode on without talking for the next couple of hours. At one point, Clint reached into his saddlebag for some jerky and handed Micah some. Not much of a lunch but it was standard fare when riding the trail.

Rabbits and quail were in abundance. Either would provide a fine meal. The thought of having both for dinner along with a pan of cornbread caused Clint's stomach to growl. Late in the afternoon, they each killed a rabbit. Clint had his shotgun, so he was in charge of the quail hunt. He killed three. Tonight, he and Micah would eat well. He hoped Micah had thought of packing some cornbread.

Their ride came to an end just at dusk. They reached the southern border of the ranch and after checking out a couple of miles of fence line, they set up camp and built a fire for dinner. The meal was just as good as Clint had imagined. And Micah had packed some cornbread! Life was

good.

Why wasn't Micah more talkative? Each evening when they were camping on the trail or in a line shack, he would watch Micah eat in almost complete silence and then get the leather-bound journal he kept in his saddlebags. After writing for twenty minutes or so, Micah would retire for the night. Odd behavior. Not like the old Micah at all. Clint noticed this change in Micah when they were in the bunkhouse as well as every other time they were camping on the trail or sleeping in a line shack. Clint didn't know what to make of this behavior. Rather than say anything, Clint just stored away this information to ponder later.

They slept under the stars listening to an occasional coyote howl at the nearly full moon. Once again, sleep came slowly for Clint. How could he account for all the changes that had been taking place in Micah? And what was he writing in his journal? Why was Micah so quiet these days? And then what was with Micah's singing? Where did his happiness come from? Why wouldn't he come partying with him at least once in a while? Had he stretched his friendship with Micah too far by hitching a ride to work every day over the past many months?

When sleep finally came, it was fitful. No problem.

Morning would come soon enough, and Clint could once again get lost in his work.

There was nothing quite like waking up while camping on the trail and making a pot of coffee over the fire—coffee usually so thick a spoon could almost stand up in it. The smell of bacon frying made his taste buds water. They typically would take along biscuits. Cold biscuits with a couple of pieces of bacon inside made for a breakfast that was hardy and would stick to their ribs until lunchtime.

After breakfast, they saddled up and spent about an hour on water well maintenance. Then it was time to slowly start bunching up the herd and getting them ready to move to the next pasture. For this move, they were able to gather all three hundred head along the fence line with Clint and Micah keeping them slowly moving forward.

The work was not hard. The cattle did most of the work. They made this trip every few months, so they knew the routine. The only new element was the addition of about a hundred new calves.

As the herd started moving, the calves followed staying close trying to suckle along the way. Every couple of hours, Clint and Micah would allow the herd to stop and graze. The average cow will spend about six hours eating grass

each day. It was also important that they allow the new calves to get plenty of milk.

Micah led the herd and Clint stayed near the back. If a cow or calf strayed, Clint would lope off in their direction and bring them back to the herd. When he was not rounding up strays, Clint was able to inspect the fence line, saving them from having to retrace their steps later.

Clint had a lot of time to think that day. As he rode, he tried to put words to what was different with Micah. He had already identified some of them. The new Micah was patient, tolerant, gentle, kind, and loving. But there was more. What else was it that was different about Micah?

The word integrity came to mind. It is not as though Micah didn't have integrity before. But now it was somehow different. Micah had always been a man of his word. He didn't steal. Yet now he could also say that Micah was morally upright. He was decent, honest, fair.

If there is one thing Clint knows about, it is integrity.

He always believed himself to be a man of integrity. Sure, he occasionally took a tool from the ranch home with him. It was not like he was stealing it. He just needed to borrow it. But he did admit more than once he forgot to bring a tool back.

Clint thought of all the married women he had run around with. Would a man of integrity do that? The more he thought of it, Clint realized he was a long way from being a man of integrity.

What were the other facets of integrity, he thought. Bottom line, someone with integrity has a moral compass that always points true north and doesn't waver. They not only know the difference between right and wrong, they always choose what is right. It doesn't matter who is watching or if they are alone. People with integrity make the right decisions day in and day out.

They got the herd to the neighboring pasture by dusk and made camp for the night. Micah built a fire as Clint put on a pot of coffee. Dinner tonight would be a couple cans of beans. The cattle were too close for them to hunt for live game. They didn't mind. Tomorrow they would head back to the bunkhouse and the dining hall and have a good meal and a soft bed.

Clint kept thinking about Micah. Micah had finally regained his integrity. It started with him admitting he was headed for no good end. When he decided he wanted to be a faithful husband, he realized it was going to mean he had to make drastic changes in his life. He was pretty sure he

needed to give up drinking since he didn't seem to have a built in "stop switch." There were so many things in his life he needed to change.

His friend of more than forty years had made remarkable changes. One of the most significant things about the changes Clint saw in Micah was the fact that Micah hadn't become a "do-gooder." He was not busy telling others how they ought to live their lives. He just quietly went about his business while he radically altered how he lived.

There were so many changes in Micah that Clint didn't know where to start in listing them all. What he did know is he liked the man Micah had become—and he wanted to see the same changes in himself.

Once again, as midnight approached, Clint found himself staring at the stars and thinking about Micah. What Clint believed is if Micah could change, he could too. He didn't know how but he was determined to figure it out.

Closing his eyes, Clint said, "I want to be a man of integrity. That will be my mission. I believe I will get there."

Little did Clint know all that would have to happen for him to finally get to that place of being a true man of integrity.

CHAPTER 7: DISCIPLINE

"Three kinds of men:
The ones that learn by reading.
The few who learn by observation.
The rest who have to pee on the electric fence
to find out for themselves."
~ Will Rogers

One day in May, Micah showed up at Clint's motel, but Clint was nowhere around. Micah knocked on his door but there was no response. Micah wasn't sure what was going on, but he went on to work and figured Clint would either come to the ranch or not.

Clint showed up as the breakfast meeting was ending. He lamely told Micah he just wasn't hungry that day. Micah could see in his eyes that Clint has pulled another long night of drinking and drugging and carousing around. Clint didn't come inside because he didn't want the other hands to know he had been on another bender the night before. It happened every week. Lately it was happening two or three times each week. But this was the first time Clint had almost missed work because of it.

Clint got in a ranch pickup with the intention of taking it out to the barn for the men who were loading a trailer

with hay. Backing into the barn Clint cut the wheel too much and crashed into the corner of the barn.

He got out to survey the damage. The truck was not hurt too much but the front fender and door on the passenger's side were dented. Not the first dents on the well-worn work truck, but the first ones placed there by Clint.

He walked back to the dining hall and told Micah what he had done. Micah just listened and nodded his head. He then shrugged his shoulders and said, "Let's get to work."

Clint followed Micah to the corral. They both saddled up and headed out to finish the fence mending in a pasture about five miles away. As they rode both men were silent.

Micah reached into his saddlebag and handed Clint a biscuit. "Just in case you get hungry later, I packed a few extra."

Clint took it and hungrily ate. He took a sideways glance at Micah, but Micah was not looking at him. He waited for Micah to give him a lecture about his responsibilities and how he needed to take better care of his job. But the lecture never came.

Arriving at the damaged fence, they dismounted and began the rebuilding process. Neither man said a thing other than a few comments about the fence or a comment about

stretching wire or locating a certain tool.

Rebuilding a barbed wire fence was not difficult but it could be time consuming.

In this case, they had to reset a number of posts. The fence was one of the older ones on the ranch. Posts had rotted so more than a dozen would have to be replaced.

Preparing for the inevitable fence mending, there were stores of posts and spools of wire in each pasture. Micah went for supplies as Clint started digging new postholes. The hard work suited him. The harder he worked the clearer his thoughts. Digging postholes was backbreaking work, especially given they hadn't gotten any rain in a couple of weeks and the ground was hard.

By the time Micah got back with the posts and wire, Clint already had eight holes dug. In spite of the cool air, Clint's shirt was soaking wet with sweat.

They set the posts and then started stringing the new wire. They spliced into the old wire and then used fence stretchers to make it taut. Each man carried a pair of fence pliers. They would use them to pull old staples, cut wire, and hammer in the new staples.

Clint and Micah were a good team. They had worked together long enough they didn't need a lot of direction and

could anticipate each other's next move.

They fixed fence all morning, then ate a few biscuits for lunch. When their meal was over, they went back to their chores.

It looked like there was about a half mile of fence that was down. With luck they would be able to complete it that day. This time Clint went for more supplies and Micah stayed behind digging more postholes. They completed their task about sundown and headed back to the corral. The horses knew the trail and could easily make it in the dark. Neither man minded working late because they knew their extra work would keep them from having to come back here for another day.

On their way back to the corral, Clint asked, "Don't you want to say anything about this morning?"

"What do you mean?" asked Micah.

"You know what I mean. You know I didn't just skip breakfast. You could tell that I was hung over. I know you could."

"You're a grown man. You have a right to live your life as you like. You still gave a good day's work. I've no complaints there. So long as you do your job, how you live your life is up to you," Micah replied.

They rode on in silence. Clint thought he would have felt better if Micah had gotten on to him about his hangover. Since Micah wouldn't oblige, Clint would have to do it himself. Over the next hour of their ride, Clint called himself every name in the book. He secretly loathed his behavior.

He hated the fact that he couldn't stop drinking or using when he wanted to. Each time Clint would tell himself, "Just one more drink," or "only one more hit." But then he would get another buzz and would try to keep it going, knowing that meant he would chase the high until the early morning hours.

Clint could work as hard or harder than any other hand. He was dependable—even though he came close to not showing up for work a couple of days before. For the most part, he kept his word and did what he said he would do. But deep inside, Clint knew he lacked the discipline he saw in Micah.

A belief that emanated deep within Clint was that he made his own breaks—that he was responsible for any good luck that came his way. He liked the phrase of "picking himself up by his own bootstraps." That suited him fine.

But as Clint took stock of his life, he realized he had

completely failed when it came to discipline. Sure, he could stay on a good path for a while, but before long, he was back to his old ways. How had Micah done it? How had he developed such discipline?

What Clint didn't know was Micah was thinking about the discipline in his life. He found discipline in his life not by following rules. When Micah entered recovery, he thought others were going to tell him how he had to live his life. He felt rule following was necessary for him to make the changes necessary.

Instead, he found recovery and sustained sobriety is not a matter of rules. Rather, it included the discipline of attending meetings, working with a sponsor, and doing Step work. These disciplines are what mattered most. Strangely, the discipline of recovery bleeds over into other parts of life.

Micah still hadn't told Clint much about his recovery life. He didn't tell him he attended meetings two or three evenings a week and often on Saturday morning. While he knew the time was coming when he would tell Clint, he didn't think Clint was ready to change yet. He didn't believe Clint had hit bottom. Only when a person hits bottom and recognizes life has become unmanageable and they are

powerless to make the changes necessary will they be ready to take the recovery journey.

With only stars to light the trail, they continued riding in silence. Lost in his own thoughts Clint looked at the stars. In his own mind, Clint said, *help me to become a man who has discipline—not just some of the time but all of the time.*

CHAPTER 8: SELF-CONTROL

"If you get to thinking you're a person of some influence, try ordering somebody else's dog around."
~ Will Rogers

Several times a year on a Friday after work, Clint would get with two or three other hands from the H&F and they would drive to Lake Charles, Louisiana, to try their hand at a little gambling. They would arrive in the early morning hours on Saturday, most times gambling straight through until Sunday evening and then travel back to the ranch, trading driving duties so the others could get some sleep. They would usually rent one room to share so they could get a couple of hours of sleep when they had the need.

Clint seemed to like gambling more than the other hands. He felt he was lucky, for the most part. He could sit for hours playing blackjack. What was not to love about the casino? There was excitement, pretty women, and free drinks so long as he was gambling. People seemed to like Clint and he certainly enjoyed the extra attention he got when he was there. He would take speed so that he could

stay awake and found he could stay alert for days on end and not miss any of the fun.

The rest of the group would usually stay together but Clint liked to be off on his own. On Sunday, if Clint was ahead, he would celebrate by taking a taxi to one of the nearby strip clubs and spend some of his winnings on some cute thing who would make him feel like he was the cock of the walk. On those weekends when Clint had lost more than he had won, he would console himself by buying sexual favors at his favorite strip club. Clint always kept a few bills folded and stuck in his wallet, so he would have what he needed to pay for sex.

The other hands noticed Clint's behavior was more extreme than theirs. He drank more, gambled larger sums of money, always took drugs to stay awake, and would invariably slip off for some female companionship during the early morning hours. Several times they would make mention of his behavior and Clint would laugh it off and comment that they just couldn't keep up with him.

The foreman and all the hands knew what he was doing. The only way he was able to keep his job when he was impaired was because of his amazing work ethic. He could work other men under the table. There was always talk about

how close Clint got in risking his job but somehow, he always seemed to come out just fine. But then things changed.

Clint knew things had gotten out-of-control when he woke up in a truck that was parked in the median of Interstate Ten in Mississippi with a paper bag beside him that contained four thousand dollars.

He didn't know how he got there or how he got the money but it was the weekend, so he knew he had been to the casino. He didn't recognize the truck he was in, but he knew it didn't belong to him or any of the hands that joined him in gambling. Frightened as to what he might have done, he abandoned the truck and hitchhiked back across Mississippi, Louisiana, and into Texas. It took him the rest of the weekend and into Monday evening to get back to Bandera.

When he finally showed up at the dining hall on Tuesday morning after being a no show on Monday, the foreman looked at his bloodshot eyes and said, "Hazard, you have just earned yourself a week off without pay. I want you to go wait for me in my office. You may be leaving here for good. I haven't decided yet."

Clint left the table with his hat in his hands and listened

to the other hands snicker as he walked out. The only thing that surprised them was that he had gotten by this long without being suspended or fired.

Waiting in the foreman's office, Clint recognized there was a good chance he would lose his job. He didn't know what he would do if that happened. He was sure things were going to be much worse for him when he finally got to trial for his DUI if it was found out he lost his job for more bad behavior that revolved around his drinking.

Clint waited more than an hour for the foreman. He knew the foreman had to finish conducting the morning meeting and getting all of the hands lined out, but he couldn't imagine why it was taking so long. Finally, the foreman arrived.

Clint stood and said, "Sir, I know…." The foreman cut him off and said, "Clint, sit down and shut up. I have put up with your shenanigans for more than twenty years. If you weren't such a good hand, you'd have lost your job many years ago. But being a good hand won't cut it any longer. I'd about decided this was the last straw and we would all be better off without you. In fact, I still think that may be the case. I can't believe you would show up in the middle of the morning meeting looking like road kill and smellin' like a

distillery. Your lack of respect for your job, for yourself, and for the other men can no longer be tolerated. I intended to come in here and write you your last check and tell you to leave the ranch and never set foot here again.

"But I sat at the table and had a cup of coffee with Micah. I don't know what he sees in you or why he's still your friend, but Micah asked me to give you another chance. I think it's a mistake. I don't think you'll ever change. You're like an overgrown boy. You're more immature then the youngest hand we've got. What's it going to take for you to grow up?"

"Well sir…."

"Don't interrupt me. I don't need an answer. You just sit and listen."

"Yes sir."

The foreman reached inside his desk and picked up a business card. "This is a therapist in Bandera that has done work over the years for some people from the ranch. You're to start therapy now and continue every week for at least three months. I am going to pay for it and the therapist will give me reports of your progress. Only by successfully completing your time there will you be able to continue your employment with the H&F."

"Do you really think that's necessary?" asked Clint. "I'll straighten up. I don't need to go to therapy."

"Hazard, this isn't your decision. You'll either go to therapy or you will end your employment with the ranch today. It's your choice. Which will it be?"

"I'll go to therapy, like you said."

The foreman told Clint he'd already made him an appointment that afternoon and every Tuesday after that for the next three months. Clint wondered how he could get appointments set up on short notice and why he even had the card of a therapist.

* * * * * * *

That afternoon, Clint succeeded in getting a cab to pick him up at the ranch and deliver him to his midafternoon appointment with the therapist. He'd thought all therapists were women. He was surprised to find from the name on the door that this was a male therapist. Somehow, he just hadn't picked up on that from the business card. He waited in the waiting room, looked at magazines, and listened to the soft music that filled the room. The longer Clint waited, the more he was sure the therapist was just making him wait to

show him who was in charge. Finally, the door to the waiting room opened.

"Hello Clint. I'm Dr. Hanson. Come in and take a seat."

Clint was feeling cocky, a bit angry about having to be there, sad about having to miss several hours of work, and flummoxed about the whole therapy process.

Clint followed Dr. Hanson into the office and took a seat. As he looked around the room, Clint began with a pissing contest. He looked at the therapist's boots and snickered. "I see from your boots that you don't spend much time on a ranch. In fact, I'll bet you don't even know how to ride a horse."

"What makes you say that?"

"I think I've seen you at the ranch once or twice through the years. You look to me more like a drugstore cowboy. You probably wear boots because you think it's expected in this town or because you're trying to pass yourself off as a 'real cowboy,' not the drugstore, Friday night café type."

"So, Clint, it seems you have some great insight into me. What do you know about yourself?"

"Doc, you don't have to go through all of that

psychobabble stuff with me. I've done this before. When I was in college, they put us through all the psychological testing and I did fine. I don't need therapy."

"In that case," Dr. Hanson said, "we can just end our session now. You are free to go. In fact, I want you to leave my office now." Dr. Hanson stood up, walked to the door, opened it, and motioned for Clint to leave.

"Oh yes, Clint, one more thing. My great-great-great-grandfather was Slim Hanson, one of the original owners of the H&F. In fact, I still own ten percent of the ranch. I think we are gonna be better off without you."

With that, Dr. Hanson led Clint back to the waiting room and closed the door. Clint was speechless for one of the few times in his life. He stood outside the closed door and suddenly reflected on what he had done. If he didn't stay in therapy, he would lose his job. And besides that, this therapist is one of the owners of the ranch.

How could he have messed up again? All he was trying to do was set the ground rules of the therapy sessions and let the therapist know that he wasn't going to put up with all the therapy nonsense. But he knew unless he could undo the mess he just made he could kiss his job goodbye.

Clint stood stunned as he contemplated what to do

next. Finally, he had a seat and hoped Dr. Hanson would come back out and give him another chance. When it became clear he was not coming out of the office, Clint tentatively knocked on his door.

After about thirty seconds, Dr. Hanson opened the door and said, "Yes?"

Clint stood holding his hat and looking at the ground. He rolled and unrolled the brim of his hat and finally said, "Doc, I'm sorry for the way I acted in there. I don't know what came over me. I guess I was just blowin' off trying to act tougher than I am. What I do know is I need help. And if I don't stay in therapy with you, I'll lose my job. I can't afford that. If you'll give me another chance, I'll try my best to be a good patient. You're in charge and not me."

Dr. Hanson listened and looked deeply into Clint's eyes. "Clint, I'll give you another chance. But this is the way things are going to go. You're right. I'm in charge. And I'll make reports once a month to your foreman. However, I'm not going to report on what happens in sessions. My reports will say you're making progress and are compliant with therapy or you are not compliant and not making progress. What you say in session stays here. But I'll need for you to talk—be willing to open up—and to drop the macho act you put

on with everyone else. If you want help, I think I can help you.

And if you just want to mark time and complete your twelve sessions so you can keep your job, then you can do that. But I hope you'll take advantage of this opportunity to do some deeper work on yourself."

"Yes sir, I'll do what you say. Thanks for givin' me another chance. You won't be sorry."

With that misstep behind him, Clint was able to begin therapy. Week after week, Clint showed up at the same time on Tuesday afternoons. For the first several weeks, it was hard for him to open up. He felt he wouldn't have anything to talk about. But then he found himself looking forward to his sessions, although he still found himself being resistant from time to time.

In the second session, Dr. Hanson revealed to Clint he was a recovering alcoholic and he knew something about the struggle Clint had been going through. Clint said, "good for you," but was not ready to talk about his alcohol abuse.

After a month of therapy, Clint finally started to let his guard down. He said he wasn't making any promises but he would try to be more open. Clint told the story of waking up in the median of Interstate Ten in Mississippi. He talked

about the blackout and the cash and having no memory. He still had the money he had evidently won gambling but didn't remember winning. Clint told how he was in a vehicle that didn't belong to him or any of his friends and of how he was fearful that he might have stolen it but simply couldn't remember.

Dr. Hanson listened and just let Clint talk as long as he was willing. "So, Clint, do you have a problem with drinking?"

Clint contemplated the question and said he didn't think so. The reason he didn't think he had a problem was he could stop drinking any time he wanted to. In fact, he told of quitting drinking several times in the past and once having gone for about a month without drinking anything.

He explained to Dr. Hanson he tried to exercise self-control and that he was cutting down on his drinking. He started by slowing down his liquor consumption, then limiting his drinking to "just beer"—though he would go through at least two six packs an evening. He said he tried cutting down on beer only to find he just didn't have the self-control necessary. He hated to admit that about himself. He thought he had the self-control to stop anything. But as he cut down on his drinking, his drug use escalated. The

more he concentrated on limiting his drug use, the more he found himself wanting to occupy his time looking at pornography on his computer.

Dr. Hanson suggested Clint might consider the fact that he was an alcoholic. Clint strongly resisted that label. "I can quit any time I want to. And only once in twenty years did my drinkin' cause me to miss work.

"So, Clint, what is an alcoholic to you?"

"That's someone like those ole booze hounds at the Cheer Up who drink themselves into unconsciousness every night. They don't know how to stop drinkin'. Most of them can't keep a job. I'm not like that at all. Actually, for the last couple of months, all I've been drinkin' is beer—except for that last weekend at the casino. And the only time I get drunk is on a Friday or Saturday evening, just to unwind from the week of work."

"What if I were to tell you that it's possible for someone to be an alcoholic and never drink anything but beer and never let their drinking jeopardize their job?" Dr. Hanson said. "We look at a number of things to determine if someone has a problem with drinking. We ask questions like, have you ever thought you need to cut down on your drinking? Have people ever annoyed you by criticizing your

drinking? Have you ever felt guilty about your drinking? Have you ever harmed yourself or someone else by your drinking behavior? Have you experienced losses in life due to your drinking? There are lots of questions that we ask to help determine if a person has a problem with drinking."

Clint said, "Thanks doc. I hear what you are sayin'. And I guess there've been times in the past when I had a problem with alcohol, but I don't have a problem now. I can control my drinkin'."

"Clint, self-control is well and good. When a person gets into recovery from addiction and enters into a solid recovery program, then they learn how to exercise self-control in many areas. But when it comes to their drinking, they recognize that they're powerless over it and need to work a program of recovery if they're ever going to be able to permanently stay away from alcohol."

"I get it doc. But I'm not an alcoholic."

As the session came to a close, Dr. Hanson told Clint that was their twelfth session and he was going to be reporting to the foreman that he had successfully completed his sessions. "And Clint, if you ever want to come back on your own, I'd be glad to once again have you as a patient."

With that, they shook hands and Clint left the therapy

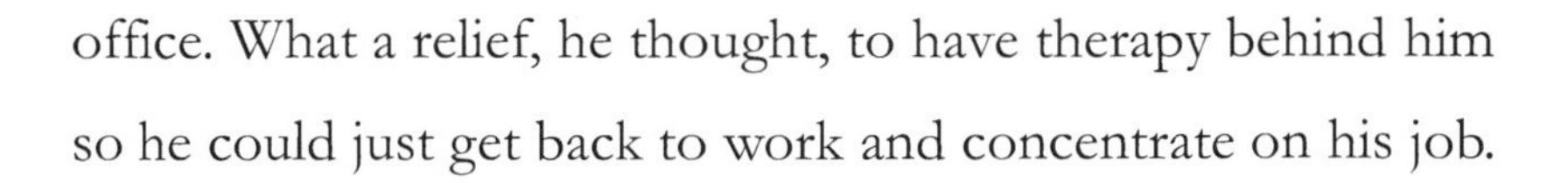

office. What a relief, he thought, to have therapy behind him so he could just get back to work and concentrate on his job.

CHAPTER 9: HEALTHY THOUGHTS

"Talk low, talk slow, and don't say too much."
~ John Wayne

With other jobs caught up, it was time to concentrate on rebuilding a couple of the game fences to keep the exotics where they belonged. For safety of the hunters, the game ranch was shut down for the first week of June and most of the hands were required to move into the bunkhouse for the week since they would be required to work close to sixteen-hour days. Trailers that contained generators and telescoping lighting towers were brought in to allow for work before and after the sun was up.

Because of the size of the ranch, hands paired up and rode to their assigned portion of the fence. In order not to startle the wild game, all the hands went to their assigned work area on horseback. Materials were even brought in by wagon, so the animals would not hear the sound of motors. The lighting units were fitted with special mufflers and were

encased in sound deadening enclosures and ran almost silently. The only intrusion for the animals was the presence of light near the fence line at times when there should have been complete darkness.
While that is also a condition they wanted to avoid, the urgency of the task dictated the extra lighting.

During the long days, Clint often fantasizes about other men's wives. And when he is around any women, he never misses an opportunity to admire them. He checks out body parts and has no shame if someone catches him objectifying them. He dreams of escaping ranch life and finding some new woman in town who is financially successful and wants a good-looking man like Clint around. He thinks about what it would be like if he could win the lottery or make a killing at the roulette tables when he and his friends make their quarterly trip to Vegas.

Fantasy has always been an escape for Clint. His constant daydreaming in high school resulted in him getting very poor grades. And for the last twenty years on the H&F, Clint found he could do most of his tasks without needing to concentrate much at all.

But it was his sexual fantasies that held the most power for him. He had several favorites he continued to go back to.

Each time he did, he could elicit feelings he judged to be close to what he would have if he were living the events instead of just fantasizing.

It was interesting to Clint when he recognized how unsatisfied with life he would get when he spent a significant portion of his day lost in fantasy. His job, which he actually loved, seemed boring. His wife, who was all he had ever really wanted, seemed dull and unimaginative. On those days, as he contemplated the future, he found he didn't have much to look forward to. Even so, Clint couldn't conceive of living without fantasy. *Fantasy is my friend*, he mused. He could change the scene, some of the supporting characters, the beginning or the ending. What was constant with his fantasies was that he was the lead character and was also the hero, the winner, the one who got the girl, the one who was admired by all.

Clint never got over the fact that even though he was a local hero during his rodeo days in high school and shortly afterwards, he was just another aging cowboy in Bandcra—a town filled with people who were more interesting, more colorful, and were making a greater impact on the world. When the dark moments came, Clint would think of himself as a has-been or a loser. But whether he was

engrossed in fantasy or depressed and thinking his best days were behind him, he would be sure to end the day at the Cheer Up or the Stumble Inn.

What bugged Clint more than anything was when he shared some of these thoughts with Micah, he was greeted mostly with silence. Clint got the distinct feeling Micah was trying hard not to lecture or criticize him. Clint pressed him. "I really need to hear something from you. You're my best friend. If I can't talk to you about my feelings, who am I going to talk with?"

Micah continued in silence as he guided his horse through the cedar thicket with Clint riding parallel to him about three yards away. When it looked like Micah was just going to keep riding as though he had not heard Clint, he spoke in a voice so quiet, Clint almost didn't hear him.

"I used to think of those things myself. I've felt like a loser many times. I've been tempted to get in my truck and just start drivin' north—maybe to Wyoming. Maybe Canada. And not tell anyone I was leaving or where I was goin'. I've had my share of pity parties."

Clint angrily said, "I'm not having a pity party!"

"Just hear me out. You wanted me to talk so do me a favor and go to listenin'. I never said you had a pity party. I

said I did. There've been many days when I was looking for more than I thought I was ever gonna get in my life here. And I'm not talkin' about money or stuff. What I'm sayin' is life didn't have much meanin' for me.

"Used to, I was either drinkin', drunk, or thinkin' about my next drink. I looked at my wife and thought she was just getting older by the day and I didn't seem to have the same spark when I touched her. But most of all, I got to thinkin' life had somehow passed me by. The worst was a day a couple of years ago when I realized I was never gonna be any more than I was then. I would never be the ranch foreman. No one was gonna leave me an inheritance, so I could buy some of the toys I've seen other men buy.

The only thing I had to look forward to was the evenings when we would meet at the Cheer Up and drink."

"And you even quit goin' out with me," Clint said. "Man, I thought you must have gotten religion or somethin' because one day you were at the Cheer Up with me and the next, you were not. You seemed to be disappearin' from my life."

"I wasn't disappearin' from *your* life. I was disappearin' from *my* life." Micah shifted his weight in the saddle and continued. "I started to have a conversation with myself. As

I looked at my life, I didn't like what I saw. My focus was on me—what made me happy, what made me sad. What I liked and what I didn't like. Over the next few days, I realized I needed to take a different direction in life if I was gonna be satisfied with me. And I also realized the new direction had nothin' to do with geography, but a whole lot to do with my focus.

"I knew I needed to make some big changes or I would always feel like life passed me by."

"So that's what you are sayin' I need to do—get a new focus on life?" asked Clint.

"No, Clint. This is not about you at all. And the reason I didn't want to say more about my life before now was I thought you would think I was tryin' to tell you how to live. How you live is up to you. I have no say in that.

"But what I realized was I needed to make some changes in my life for me to even like the man that I am. That's all I am sayin'. I've just been tryin' to look at life differently. And for me, it has been workin'. The most important change I made was to stop drinkin'. And Clint, I'm not sayin' anything about you. This is about me. I realized I didn't want the highlight of my life to be when I got off work and had the first of many drinks."

Silently, both men continued riding. Micah was talked out and Clint didn't have anything to say back to him. He still felt Micah was trying to meddle in his life—trying to tell him he was on the wrong road. But the more Clint thought about what Micah said, he realized Micah was just talking about himself. And he had simply answered when Clint pushed him to respond to his own depressive thoughts.

Clint watched Micah as he rode on. There were times when he thought Micah had the beginnings of a smile, like he was telling himself a joke or was reliving some wild evening. But the more Clint thought about it, he realized Micah had that same look—call it satisfied or contented—for most of the past two years. Something was going on with him, Clint thought. He wasn't sure what it was, but something was certainly different about Micah.

Clint knew Micah had stopped drinking and he was just waiting for Micah to start preaching to him and the rest of the men about their misguided ways and the evils of alcohol.

But he never did. Clint realized Micah had just decided for himself not to drink and didn't try to convince anyone else to change.

The two cowboys had known each other their whole lives. Silence between them was not uncomfortable. And on

this occasion, they continued riding in silence for the better part of an hour. Yet the silence this time seemed different. It was as though there was a lot to be said and neither of them knew how to start or what to say.

Finally, when Clint could stand it no longer, he said, "I've been noticing you're always writin' in that book you keep in your saddlebag. I know it's not ranch business because you always record that on the computer. What are you writin'?"

Micah reached behind his saddle. "You mean this?"

"Yeah. What're you writin'?" Clint asked.

"I've been keepin' a journal for the past year or so."

"What's a journal?"

"It's just a record of what happens during the day along with my thoughts and feelin's. This is how I've kept the conversation with myself goin'."

"What good's that?"

"Well, I've found when I have a record of events I can go back and take stock of how I have been livin'. I like to see how my mood changes from day to day. It's also good to remind me of my thoughts over time.

"When I stopped drinkin', I realized I needed to do something else to occupy my time as well as my thoughts. At

first, all I could think of was wantin' to get off work and pop the top on a six-pack or two. Soon I knew I was gonna have to change my thought patterns if I was going to be successful in changin' my behavior. Writin' in my journal helps.

"I've actually found I like goin' back every few days and readin' what I wrote. Clint, I can tell you, what I found really surprised me. You talk about messed up! My thoughts were a mess and I never realized it."

About half an hour later, they arrived at the corral, unsaddled their horses, and went to dinner. Clint didn't sit with Micah. He wasn't mad at him, but he needed to be away from him so he could think. Clint chatted up several of the other hands. They talked about the day and how glad they were they would be able to complete the emergency fencing job in a week. Dinner ended and quickly most of the hands retired to the bunkhouse.

****

The starlight was brilliant as Clint came out of the bunkhouse.

Usually, he would head to town, drink and party until

there was no one else willing to indulge him. Tonight, he just walked out by the corral. He wasn't sure what was happening with him. All he knew was life was not as great as he'd been telling himself. Partying was fun. At least it had been twenty years ago. Now on the north side of forty, he realized he was chasing something he never had. He was looking for meaning. For fulfillment. For contentment.

The thoughts startled him. He'd never felt contented. How would he know when he found contentment? There had to be something greater than himself, but he didn't know who or what that was. His thoughts troubled him. He always thought of himself as the greatest force to be reckoned with. What was with all of the spiritual thoughts he had been having? What was bigger than him? He didn't believe in God. But there had to be something else in life he was not finding.

An hour later, he silently tiptoed into the bunkhouse trying not to wake anyone. The lights in the bunkhouse were on timers. They normally went out at exactly ten each evening and were programmed to come on at five in the morning. But for this job as well as during calving season, the lights went off at nine and came on again at four.

He crept to his bunk in the dark, took off his boots and

jeans and lay down. Try as he might, he found it difficult to sleep. Finally, just a few hours before the lights were to come on, Clint drifted off into a restless sleep. His last thoughts were of his friend and how he seemed so contented. Clint wondered if he would ever know the same sense of contentment.

CHAPTER 10: NEITHER SELFISH NOR SELF-CENTERED

"If you're riding ahead of the herd,
take a look back every now and then to
make sure it's still there."
~ Old West Proverb

Branding has been used for hundreds of years for marking livestock. With the protests of animal rights advocates through the years, the H&F had experimented with other ways of marking their cattle including tattoos to ears and the inner lip. They even used freeze branding for a while. But branding is so intractably connected to the cowboy culture that the alternate methods of marking cattle were not used for long on the ranch.

At the same time as branding, calves are castrated, vaccinated, and given an ear tag. Proponents of branding say ear tags have made brands obsolete, but ranchers still prefer to be able to identify the cattle they own by a visible brand and not have to resort to a barcode reader or registration book to decode ear tags.

June was branding time on the H&F and it would always take on a bit of a festive atmosphere. Most of the calves are

kept in pens near headquarters after their birth until branding is over.

Typically, this is done when the calves are two to three months old. That means most of the hands are able to work together for the week or so it took for branding. The hands love to laugh and often take the edge off their work by trading jokes and insults with each other. There's always plenty of laughing and lots of whooping and hollering as the cowboys use their horses to carefully cut the calves from the herd.

One cowboy will rope the calf, give the rope a turn around his saddle horn, and walk the calf over to where the branding irons are kept hot in a partially enclosed, propane-fired oven that resembles a kiln. Then another cowboy throws a loop down low to rope the calf's back legs. The calf is stretched out on the ground and a team of hands quickly works on the calf. One person applies the brand. Another gives the calf vaccinations to provide immunity from various viruses that impact health and beef production. Another applies the ear tag. Then another hand castrates the calves.

During branding, the hands generally didn't stop for lunch. Instead they would work until they're tired, then take

a break only to get some water or eat a piece of beef jerky. Sometimes sandwiches were brought out to the picnic tables between the stable and headquarters. Guests from the dude ranch line the fence surrounding the corral to watch the cowboys work.

These were always long days of work. Clint felt he worked harder than Micah, or anyone else for that matter. He even liked the audience from the dude ranch guests.

A bit of a showboat ever since his time of rodeoing, Clint could put on a show. He would swing his hat at the cattle more than necessary, let out more whoops and whistles than were needed, and would generally be in a position where his adoring audience could see him work.

The other hands noticed his preening for the guests. They often kid him about his showmanship. But Clint takes it in stride and tells them he feels obligated to let the guests see a good show and to see how real cowboys work.

Dinner each evening during branding time features an appetizer that is a ranch favorite—mountain oysters, known by many names including calf fries, Rocky Mountain oysters, cowboy caviar, prairie oysters, and Montana tendergroins. Whatever the name, the cowboys line up to get a plate of deep fried calf testacies and a little bowl of cocktail sauce

for dipping. Guests from the dude ranch often join the cowboys as they partake of this delicacy that is always served up on the picnic tables, weather permitting.

When the dinner bell sounded, Clint elbowed himself to the front of the line. He got his pick of the steak being served—usually taking two. He believed since he was the hardest working hand, he should have the best steaks. He wasn't too proud to slide several steaks around in the big serving pans until he found the ones that suited him.

He was always the first in line for dessert. Often, he would be finishing his steak and thinking about seconds when he would see Micah at the end of the line, joking with some of the other hands, patiently waiting his turn. *How can he stand being last?* Clint thought. *I'm not going to risk them running out of food*, though he would have to admit that event never happened on the H&F. Clint didn't see that as being selfish. He just felt he needed to take care of himself first. He reasoned no one else was going to do it for him.

Clint always did a good job of looking out for himself, whether it was in the dining hall, or getting his pick of beds in the bunkhouse, or in picking out the best horse in the remuda at times when his own mount needed a break. Clint made sure he got the best there was to offer.

He could remember when he was living with his wife that she complained he didn't seem to have any regard for others. She had even called him selfish on occasion, though he thought that was really crossing the line.

His "Clint first" policy could be seen in many areas of his life. For example, his pickup—the one he had to sell because of his recent legal trouble—was the best pickup in Bandera. He got the special towing package, the big tires, heavy-duty suspension, the hopped-up engine, special paint, and a killer sound system. The interior was not only leather but was the best leather available. Although he paid more than sixty thousand dollars for it three years ago, Clint felt that it was an investment and he was proud of the purchase.

On the other hand, his wife drove a well-worn SUV they bought used several years before. Clint didn't see anything wrong with this since he was the one making the living and he felt he had done a good job providing for his family. Although his wife didn't complain about having a nearly worn out vehicle, others around town noticed Clint wanted the best of everything—even if it meant his wife did without. And it was the same when his son was living at home. He would make sure he had several new pair of jeans, shirts, and a new pair of boots every year, whereas there

were several years his son didn't have new clothes to begin the school year simply because there was not money enough for that purchase.

From Clint's point of view, he was not being selfish. He was simply making sure his priorities were straight. And taking care of Clint came first.

Chapter 11: Not Judgmental

"If you are riding a high horse
there ain't no way to get down off it gracefully."
~ Cowboy Wisdom

Jericho has worked on the ranch more than fifty years. He started as a wrangler when he was nineteen and was a top hand for years. He even became a section boss after some time. He never married. It was said in his day he would out work and out drink all contenders.

About twenty years before, a horse busted him up. They were rounding up cattle that had been grazing in a cedar grove. A rattlesnake spooked his horse and he was thrown. The fall broke several bones in his right arm and his horse came down on his left leg, crushing it. While he eventually healed, he was never able to ride again. He lived full time on the ranch in a little cabin not far from the corral. In the mornings, the wranglers would gather on his porch because they knew he would have coffee for them. They would sit and drink together for half an hour, then the wranglers would start rounding up horses.

Jericho would drive an old jeep around the paddock, honking the horn. Slowly the horses would start walking toward the corral. They knew the horn meant they were about to be fed a bucket of oats. All the wranglers needed to do was open the gate to the corral. Slowly the horses would enter and walk to the place along the fence where they always ate. Each horse had its own place. One by one the wranglers would place a halter on each horse, clip it into a lead rope that was hanging at that post, and give each a bucket of oats.

The wranglers would saddle enough horses for the cowboys first and then have the guests' horses ready for their first morning ride. There was one horse that always held back and wouldn't go into the corral until all the other horses were in their places. The wranglers knew she was afraid of the other horses and would always be the last into the corral and the last to eat. She was not used as a cow pony any more, but she was a good stable mount for guest trail rides. Always on trail rides she would only ride in last place.

After helping round up the horses, Jericho would leave his coffee duties with the wranglers and then head to the kitchen. He helped in the kitchen and dining hall at every

meal. After that, he stayed busy keeping the barns in shape. But his real gift and value to the ranch was working the guest ranch. Each morning he would greet the guests as they came to the dining hall. After breakfast, he would hang around the lodge and entertain children with stories of western folklore. In the evenings, he was always around the campfire making sure everyone had marshmallows and telling jokes to all who would listen. He told the same jokes every week since there was a new crop of guests every few days.

"What do you call a cow with no legs? Ground beef." People would laugh. Children especially liked his jokes.

"What do you call a cow that has given birth to a calf? Decaffeinated." As the laughter grew, more guests would gather around.

"What do you call a cow on a hillside? Lean beef. And I've got one more cow joke. What do you call a cow behind a bush? Cow hide."

The guests thoroughly enjoyed the entertainment. Jericho was a real ambassador for the ranch. "What's the difference between a cowboy and a mutual fund? A mutual fund will eventually mature and be able to support the family." And with that Jericho would head out to one of the

barns to straighten up tools or equipment.

His day started at four and lasted until he went to bed at ten. Occasionally one of the cowboys would tell him it was not right he had to work such long hours. But he pointed out since his accident two decades before he was never given any work assignments but was allowed to do just what he wanted. He didn't think of his days as being full of work but being filled doing just what he wanted to do. And each day after lunch he usually wanted to take a nap and he didn't need to ask permission. He did just as he pleased. He was an invaluable asset to the ranch.

Clint liked Jericho and had started working on the ranch just before his accident. One of the things that struck him about Jericho was that he never heard him say anything negative about anyone. Clint knew the same couldn't be said of him. He regularly had strong words to say about the other hands. Some he thought of as lazy. Others he considered conceited. There are some he dismissed as "lightweights." They weren't real cowboys at all but were city folk he felt couldn't cut it by getting a job in Bandera, so they came out to the ranch, keeping some deserving "real" cowboy from a job. It struck him as funny he had such negative thoughts about literally everyone he met. He sized

them up and, in his own mind, believed himself to be better than all of them.

As Clint thought about Jericho, he realized Micah had also become much less judgmental. In fact, he had not heard Micah say anything derogatory about anyone in more than a year. There was a time when Micah had some really hard words for the men but that had changed.

Clint wished he was known as being more accepting of others. But he just couldn't seem to help making snap judgments. Even when he kept his mouth shut, he still passed judgment.

CHAPTER 12: SLOW TO TAKE OFFENSE

"Never ride another man's horse without his permission and never put on another man's hat."
~ Unknown

By nature, Clint was quick-tempered. Always spoiling for a fight, Clint was quick with his words and sometimes even quicker with his fists. He didn't take anything off anyone. He was a real man, he told himself. No one was going to push him around or make him do something he didn't want to do.

More than once, Clint's short temper and impulsive nature have caused him problems. He knows he probably would have been promoted to section boss at least ten years earlier if not for his temper. Micah was promoted back then, and they hired in at exactly the same time. Clint told himself it didn't matter to him; he really didn't care. But he did care. He wanted his son to look up to him since he knew Tripp held him in contempt.

In high school, Clint was always the first one to throw a punch. He found out early in life a punch didn't hurt that

much. His father taught him that. He had been punched enough by his father he didn't think twice about tangling with any kid who was older, bigger, or stronger.

Clint knew if he threw the first punch, more often than not he would win.

He took pride all his life that he had never lost a fight. As a young hand, he would take on all comers. It didn't matter that fighting was forbidden on the ranch. He knew fights that broke out usually didn't get reported and that code of silence kept him from losing his job on many occasions.

Now at middle age, Clint wondered if he would live by his fists for the rest of his life. Was he always going to have such a thin skin? He looked at Micah and knew that even before he sobered up and cleaned up his life, he had stopped having fistfights when he was about twenty. Sure, he still lost his temper some, but he didn't resort to solving things with his fists.

But in the past two years, Clint had noticed that Micah seldom got angry. And he never saw him lose his temper any more. How could one man change so much? What was the secret to Micah's personality transplant? That is the way Clint thought of Micah, like he had a whole new personality

to replace the old one. What was going on with Micah?

****

The ground was parched and dusty after ten weeks with no rain.

Daily chores for all hands included hauling hay to feed the hungry cattle. The wells were struggling to produce enough water for the herd to survive. Fields had slowly been reduced to trampled straw. Cracks in the dirt widened. Several head had fallen into some of the wider cracks, breaking legs and had to be put down.

At the first loss, there were no tears. That just meant the cowboys would eat well for the next several days. Jubilation turned to despair as the hands realized the drought might mean an end to their jobs. No cattle, no work, and no pay!

To make matters worse, the hands got wind that the foreman was going to sell off about ten percent of the herd. If that was true, it meant he would be laying off some of the hands. While that had never happened before on the H&F, they figured this might be the time.

Clint had heard the rumor of reducing the herd and possible layoffs. Micah told him not to worry. If either of

those were going to happen, Micah and the other section bosses would know. Still Clint worried. While he had more seniority than most of the hands, he knew he was getting older and might not seem like such an asset with so many younger men willing to work for less. Clint also knew his work had been slipping some in recent months.

Panic would be the wrong word to describe the attitude of the hands. But they were very worried about their future and whether they would have jobs.

They knew there was a lot of unemployment in the area. Jobs were hard to come by. And if the H&F laid off hands, it was a sure bet none of the other ranches would be hiring.

The dry weather brought about another set of problems. Many fences were down due to cows straining against them to get to grass on the other side. That meant moving the cattle to other pastures. With nearly twenty thousand head to move, every hand was expected to stay at the ranch until all the moves could take place. Many of the hands would sleep in line shacks during the move to keep from having to come all the way back to the bunkhouse.

The foreman told the men to figure on staying on the ranch around the clock for the next two weeks. When they

weren't moving cattle, they would be hauling hay or rebuilding fences. Every hand was needed.

For those two weeks in August, breakfast was served at 4:30 and hands were in the saddle by five. No lunch was served in the dining hall. Everyone was expected to pick up a lunch sack handed out at breakfast. For those who would be staying in line shacks, they were expected to pack enough food for all their meals. It was clearly understood that lunch was just to be long enough to eat. Every man was expected to work until there was not enough light to see.

The days were long; the summer heat relentless. Less than a week into the new but temporary routine, three of the young hands, recent hires all, quit saying they didn't know what they were signing up for.

The seasoned hands chuckled and said while drought didn't happen every year, each summer they all stayed on the ranch for two weeks to move all the cattle and repair fences.

The foreman had anticipated the attrition and had hired on half a dozen additional hands. He told each their jobs were temporary, but the best of the bunch might get a permanent job. That was good motivation. The temporary hires worked hard and proved to be good hands.

Micah took his crew out to a management area about a

two-hour ride from the corral. As usual, Clint was at his side and shared in helping to make certain every hand had the tools and supplies for the fence work. Others on Micah's crew were responsible for moving hay into the new pasture.

By mid-day, the crew was well on the way to bunching up the cattle and getting them moved to the adjoining pasture. Most of the hands had already reached into their saddlebags for something to eat. They would not even dismount for lunch but would eat as they rode.

Clint looked up from his duties to see an unusual sight. The general foreman had his horse in a slow cantor and was headed right for them. While the foreman would come out to any of the pastures to check on jobs, for the most part he relied on the reports he received from his section bosses.

An ill wind blew as the foreman approached Clint. He knew what was coming. He was going to be fired. He didn't know for sure why.

But he figured it was either for wrecking the ranch pickup or for fights he continued to engage in. Or it could be for his derisive comments to the cook.

He steeled himself for the inevitable. "I've had my eye on you. Now Micah tells me I've been right about you!" Clint couldn't believe it. How could Micah have turned on

him? What had he done to him?

Clint's head spun as he tried to absorb the words of the foreman. Quickly, Clint ran through events of the past few days and weeks to see if he could light on the most likely reason he was going to be dismissed. He came up with nothing.

The foreman stopped his horse and invited Clint and Micah to join him. As they did, Clint noticed a half grin on Micah's face. He was enjoying this immensely. Clint glared at him as he climbed down. There was nothing to do now other than face whatever was coming.

"Do you know why I'm here?" asked the foreman.

"I reckon I do. But I hafta tell you I didn't see this comin'," replied Clint.

"So why do you think I'm here?"

"To fire me, of course."

With that Micah and the foreman doubled over laughing.

The longer they laughed, the angrier Clint got. They could tell Clint was getting ready to mouth off in a most inappropriate way. Finally, the foremen got control of himself and stepped toward Clint.

"I've been needing another section boss. I think you're

the guy. Micah agrees. Starting today you will be getting the same pay as a section boss. You'll keep working with Micah for at least the next month. Learn from him. When he thinks you're ready, I'll take you to the northwest corner of the ranch and introduce you to the men you'll supervise—though I think you already know most of them—and I'll explain your new duties.

"As you know, that is the hardest part of the ranch to work. The two water wells in that area are about shot and need to be replaced. Since there are roads bordering two sides of that area, that fence needs to be better maintained than the interior fences. Cows always seem to be getting out and onto the roads. We have lost several head that have just wondered off and couldn't be found. But of greatest concern to me is the traffic hazard that creates. I can't afford to have some unsuspecting driver hit one of our cows at night. I'll be expecting you to get the entire exterior fence in your area replaced before the end of the year. That is in addition to the rest of the work you'll need to do."

Slowly a grin began to spread across Clint's face. This is what he had always wanted. He was eager to show the foreman what he could do and that he was worthy of the trust he was placing in him.

The rest of the day flew by. Clint was so happy he found himself whistling as he went about his work. They finished their work just before dusk and headed toward the corral. They knew they would be able to follow the trail easily since the moon had just risen.

When they got to the dining hall, Clint was handed a note that someone had called and wanted him to return the call just as soon as possible. He excused himself from the table and went outside to find the landline phone he could use. Cell service is almost nonexistent on the ranch.

He didn't recognize the number but when the phone was answered, he recognized the voice. His attorney told him he was pretty sure the trial will be soon and that it looks like he will not only have to serve time, but he would probably be facing hard time in prison.

There was a time when prison in Texas meant a person was going to Huntsville. And that was still the place many criminals were taken. But there were other prisons all around the state. And Clint knew many of the men in them were there for repeated DUIs.

Just when he was beginning to see things turn around it looked like he was going to lose everything—finally promoted and within six hours realized he was going to

become a convicted criminal.

Clint had been living in a fantasy if he just didn't think about his approaching court date, maybe it would just fade away. He also had fantasized the charges against him would be dismissed or some extraordinary thing would happen to make this nightmare go away. But he now had to face the reality his life was getting ready to change.

He was angry. So angry that when a man stumbled into him later in the dining hall Clint raised his fists and delivered three quick blows to the stunned cowboy. Several men nearby jumped up and pulled Clint off the injured ranch hand.

The foreman was swift in his punishment for he wanted to make an impression on the other hands. "That'll be a five hundred dollar fine and a three-day suspension without pay."

Clint picked up his hat and stormed out the door. The foreman followed him and told him anything like that in the future would not only mean he would not get the section boss job he had been promised but he would be fired on the spot.

For the next three days, Clint moped around the tiny room of his motel. The first night he got so drunk he passed out with his clothes on lying on the dingy carpet.

The whole next day he drank and cursed his luck. That evening and the following day, he continued to drink so he didn't have to face the sorry state of his life.

He wanted to find someone he could blame. At first, he was mad at the cowboy who stumbled into him in the dining hall. If he hadn't started the fight, Clint wouldn't have been fined or suspended. He was also mad at his foreman. In one day he gave him a promotion and the very same day he suspended him. And he fined him five hundred dollars that Clint didn't have! All his extra money had gone to pay his lawyer.

Most of all, Clint was mad at his attorney. He knew he was of no account from the time he hired him. He should have gotten a better attorney, but he couldn't afford it. If his attorney had done a better job he could have gotten the charges against him dismissed.

There was only one person Clint didn't blame. Himself. It never occurred to him that he was responsible for every one of his DUIs. He was responsible for his short temper that led to many fights through the years and finally to his suspension. But in his drunken stupor, all he could do was find others to blame.

When evening came, Clint was tired of being drunk, so

he decided to take a walk to sober up. He figured he walked ten miles or more that evening. When he finally returned to his room, he was clear-headed. He decided to take one more walk. He walked a few blocks away to the little café where he had only eaten one other time.

To his surprise the food was good. He had his favorite, chicken fried steak and sides of several vegetables. He ordered a beer but before it came changed to iced tea. He couldn't remember when he had last ordered iced tea.

Back in his room, he turned on the TV and tried to find something that would hold his interest. Nothing came close to entertaining him. He thought about how his life had come unraveled. How could he have had so much going for him only to see it disappearing right before his eyes?

At midnight, he was staring at the ceiling again trying to sleep. For the first time he started to consider how much he was to blame for his circumstances. Maybe it was not bad breaks and it wasn't somebody else's fault. Maybe he had brought all of this on himself.

Clint knew in the morning Micah would be waiting for him out front, ready to give him a lift to work. Good old Micah. He could always count on him.

But the next morning, Micah did not come pick him up.

Five stretched to five-thirty and still Micah was not there. Clint started frantically calling taxis hoping to find someone who was willing to take him to work. Finally, he convinced one cabby to give him another chance. He made it to work just before six when the morning ranch meeting was breaking up.

The foreman met him as he was getting out of his cab. The foreman said, “Clint, you are running out of chances. Not only are you fighting and setting a bad example for the younger hands but today after your suspension you don’t even think enough of your job to show up for the meeting.”

“I’m really sorry about that. I thought I had a ride lined up, but it didn’t pan out. That will not happen again. If you’ll give me another chance, you’ll not be sorry you did.”

The foreman relented and told him to join Micah who was already walking toward the corral.

Clint hurriedly moved toward the corral. As Clint caught up he said, “Mornin’.” Micah was silent. Clint knew this was going to be a tough day.

They saddled up and rode to the pasture where they had been working. They would be about an hour in the saddle. Clint waited for what he was sure was going to be an explosion from Micah. But the explosion never came.

As they began their fence building, Clint said, "Micah, I'm sorry. I know I let you down."

In a calm but stern voice, Micah replied, "Yes, you did. Clint, you let a lot of people down. I've stood by you and run interference with the foreman more times than I can count. Other men have stuck their necks out for you. Your own son has had to make excuses for you for times when you would get in fights or come to work late.

"There are two other people you have let down big time. One is your wife. She didn't deserve what you've done to her. You've been making a laughing stock of her for more than 20 years. I don't know why she's stayed with you."

"Look, Micah. There is another side of things. You don't know what she is like to live with. And another thing; I wouldn't be in this mess now if my attorney had done his job."

"Clint, I'm tired of hearing you blame others for your problems. It's not your wife's fault. It's not your attorney's fault. And it's not your son's fault or the other men's fault and it's not my fault. You've only got one person to blame, Clint. And that's you! You did all of this to you.

"I said there were two people you let down and one was your wife. The other person is you. You have let yourself

down. I thought you were made of better stock. You're destroying yourself and you'll do your best to take everyone near you down with you. I'm tired of it. I'm not going to let you take me down. We'll still work together but I can no longer call you my friend."

Clint listened in stunned silence. He couldn't believe what he was hearing. Micah was his longest and best friend. They had been through everything together through the years. He couldn't bear the thought of losing his friendship.

With tears in his eyes, Clint said, "Micah, you're right. I've messed up big time and I don't have anyone to blame but me. Over the past three days I've blamed everyone I could think of. I went on a bender where I wasn't sober at all until last night. I started to realize last night it was my fault, but it never really got through to me until now. It's all my fault."

Clint then told Micah of the call with his attorney and of the fact that he knew he was going to have to serve time in prison. Micah listened as Clint recounted the last three days of being drunk beyond anything he had ever experienced before. He told Micah how much he wanted to change and how he was finally at a place where he had to admit he didn't know how.

"Micah, I would change if I knew how. I've made promises to myself so many times that I was gonna stop all of my bad behavior, but I always came back to it. I've taken the pledge not to drink again but usually broke it the same day. I've even made vows to God I was gonna stop cheatin'—and I meant them. But then I would find myself chasin' someone I wasn't even interested in just to make another conquest.

"I don't know what to do next. And I'm not talkin' about prison. I deserve that sentence for all the DUIs I've had. Not only have I been arrested three times, but there were other times when I was stopped while drivin' drunk and the deputy let me off with a warnin'. And there were many more times I drove under the influence and didn't get caught.

"I just don't know how to start puttin' my life in order. Where do I start?"

Micah just listened. The silence hung between them for what seemed like a long time. In reality it was probably only a couple of minutes.

"Let me think about what you've told me," said Micah. "I don't know if there is anything I can do or not. Before I even offer, I want to see how serious you are about wantin'

to change."

"Oh, I'm dead-level serious, Micah."

"Seems like I have heard you say things like that before. Somehow, I'm not convinced this time is any different. But if you are serious, let's talk again tomorrow. There may be something I know of that can help you."

For the first time in days, Clint had a glimmer of hope. He couldn't imagine what Micah had in mind. Whatever it was, Clint was eager to hear it. He wanted desperately for life to change. If only he could get started in the right way.

That night, Clint thought more about his conversation with Micah. He started to go to an angry place because Micah had called him out on his behavior. But then he remembered the calm voice and how even with what he had done, Micah was not raging at him. In fact, he realized Micah was really very slow to take offense with anyone. Clint wanted to be like that. He wanted other people to be able to consider his actions and say the same of him.

Once more, staring at the ceiling of his tiny motel room, Clint spoke, breaking the silence in the room. "I don't know how to get there but make me a man who is slow to take offense. That's what I'd really like to be."

Chapter 13: Daily Look for Joy

"Worry is like a rockin' horse.
It's something to do that
don't get you nowhere."
~ Old West Proverb

Summer was over, but the hot days were not. Over the past several weeks crews had been feeling the effects of the heat. Today's forecast was for another record high.

The bedraggled crew spent the day building fence—five-strand barbed wire fence. This had been the standard for all new fencing on the ranch for the past ten years. Thick posts were set deep—a job made more efficient by the tractor mounted post hole digger.

With the posts in place, the crew would start stringing the wire, one long strand at a time. Each wire was stretched tight between the corner post and another post that had extra bracing so as not to give under the strain. They would then use their fence pliers to staple the wire to each post.

This was repeated with each wire. When completed, each wire was so taut that it could be plucked like a guitar. This type of fence would last for years and require the least

maintenance.

By their estimate, they had built just less than a mile of fence that day. Even with the tractor digging the post holes, the work was still backbreaking, a task not made easier by temperature over ninety degrees with humidity to match.

If rain didn't come soon, surely the rumored cattle sale and layoffs would become reality. This time of year, the hands were able to get an extra hour of work in since the days were so long. The crew worked until twilight and headed for the corral.

On the way to the corral, Micah rode his horse up close to Clint's. The other men were far enough that they couldn't hear what was being said.

"Are you still serious about wantin' to change your life?" asked Micah.

"I sure am. I'll do whatever it takes. I have to change and change now, or I know I'll be the same messed up man for the rest of my life."

"If you're truly serious about wantin' to change then there is somewhere I want you to go. Saturday morning, I'll pick you up at 9:30 at the motel. If you still want to change your life, be waitin' out front. If you're not there, I'll know you've changed your mind. And if you do, that's fine. It's

your choice. No one's forcing you to make this decision."

"I'll be there, Micah. You can count on me. I'll be there. And Micah—thanks!"

They rode on to the corral and took care of their horses. Clint's taxi was waiting for him. He got in and rode back to his shabby room. Along the way, he wondered where Micah was going to take him. What did he have in mind? Micah was a bit cryptic with his instructions. Clint didn't care. All he cared about was having a chance to change his life.

As he lay in bed that night, Clint thought more about the brief conversation with Micah. He also reflected on the work they'd done that day. In spite of the heat and the long hours, Clint noticed a slight smile on Micah's face several times during the day. It was as if Micah knew something funny that no one else knew. It was the same smile he had noticed on Micah from time to time over the past year.

As he thought more about it, Micah's smile was not like he was laughing at a joke. It was more like there was some inner joy present in spite of circumstances. Where had that joy come from? How did Micah seem to find it every day?

Clint closed his eyes. Just before falling asleep, Clint said, "Help me to look for the joy that is all around me. I

know it is there. I just need to find it." With that, he drifted off into a deep sleep.

* * * * * * *

When Saturday morning came around, Clint was waiting out front of the motel fifteen minutes early. He was excited but also a bit fearful. Where was Micah going to take him? He didn't know and really didn't care. What he knew was he trusted Micah and he knew Micah was able to change his life. Maybe he could show Clint how to change his as well.

When Micah arrived, Clint eagerly climbed in the cab of the pickup. Micah reached over and turned off the key and then turned and faced Clint.

"The meetin' we are going to," began Micah, "has some rules. I need to tell you what they are before we go and see if you are willin' to abide by 'em."

"OK. Whatever they are, I'll follow them."

"The rules are that you can never tell anyone who is at the meetin'. You're gonna see several men you know and probably some that you've never met but may have seen around town. Regardless of whether you know them or not, you can never tell anyone else who you saw at the meetin'."

"I can do that," replied Clint.

"The other rule is that you cannot tell anyone what was said at the meetin'. Things that are said there or done there have to stay there. Can you agree to keep confidential what you hear?" asked Micah.

"Yes, I'll do that. You can trust me on that."

Micah restarted the truck and headed into town. Clint was expecting a church service. He secretly took a long drink from his bottle of sour mash before Micah picked him up and then chewed a piece of peppermint candy to cover the smell of the alcohol. He felt he was going to need the drink just so he would have the courage to stand up to what the church folks were dishing out.

They arrived at the bank and parked around back. Then they took the stairs to the second floor. To his surprise, they weren't going to a church service at all. In the room were about twenty men, some from surrounding ranches and others from town. He knew most of them. But what surprised him most was the atmosphere in the room. They were talking and laughing. They were acting like they were at a party but there was no booze. Even in his alcohol-numbed state, Clint could tell everyone else was sober. He couldn't put his finger on what the different was except that they all

had some of the inner joy he had noticed in his friend Micah.

The meeting began with a man standing up and saying, "Good morning gentlemen. This is the regular Saturday morning meeting of Alcoholics Anonymous. My name is Gus. I'm an alcoholic and the secretary of this meeting."

"Hello Gus," all the men said in unison.

Clint sat riveted as he listened.

"Alcoholics Anonymous is a fellowship of men and women who share their experience, strength and hope with each other that they may solve their common problem and help others to recover from alcoholism. The only requirement for membership is a desire to stop drinking. There are no dues or fees for AA membership; we are self-supporting through our own contributions. AA is not allied with any sect, denomination, politics, organization or institution; does not wish to engage in any controversy; neither endorses nor opposes any causes. Our primary purpose is to stay sober and help other alcoholics to achieve sobriety."

So, this is where Micah had been going on Saturday mornings. He was probably going to other meetings on those nights when he told Clint he had a meeting to go to

but didn't explain further.

Clint listened as several men spoke about their week and how they had struggled to stay sober and what they did to keep from drinking. Most of the men had the same buoyant attitude Micah exhibited over the past year.

Then Clint listened as Micah spoke. Micah told of how his life had changed over the past year and how grateful he was to have found AA. He told of some struggles and said he knew even though he had not had anything to drink for more than a year he was not cured. He would have to remain in recovery for the rest of his life. Micah told the group he didn't have any guarantee that he would be sober for the rest of his life but what he did know is he was going to remain sober for today. Tomorrow, he intended to focus on staying sober for that day and he would continue, one day at a time for the rest of his life.

Clint was inspired by the stories he heard. At first, he found himself thinking he wasn't like these men. While things were out of control in his life, he hadn't done the things some of these guys had done. But as he listened, he realized he was just like them. Every person there had admitted their lives had become unmanageable and they were powerless over their addiction. He also realized there

was something else he had in common with each one. That is, they all wanted to stop—stop drinking, stop using, and stop all the many out-of-control behaviors that were part of their addiction.

Toward the end of the meeting, the secretary said, "If there are any new members, would you please stand and introduce yourself by your first name only. A new member is anyone who has a desire to stop drinking and is within their first thirty days of attending AA."

Clint slowly rose to his feet. All eyes turned to him. Slowly and deliberately he said, "My name's Clint and I'm an alcoholic."

When he finished speaking, the room erupted in applause. Micah stood beside him and clapped him across the back.

As the meeting adjourned, it seemed as if every man came up to Clint and told him they were glad he was there. Many of the men he had partied with in years past approached him with big grins and said, "We've been wondering when you'd show up. We're glad you're here."

That day was the last day Clint drank any alcohol. He also stopped using and realized he was going to have to address his gambling and running around or he was going to

go back to drinking and drugging.

Clint felt like he had finally come home. He realized he had been searching for something his entire life. Still he was not sure what it was, but he was convinced he could now find it with the help of the many sober friends he made in AA. He knew he had a lot of work to do. But he was also certain he was finally on the road that would allow him to make the changes he needed to make.

He thought about what he had been noticing in Micah's life over the past year. Micah had many qualities Clint wanted badly. With the support of the other men in AA, he felt certain he could quit drinking and using for good. And through his recovery, Clint felt he could start working on his character defects and become the man he wanted to be.

That night as he lay in bed in his tiny room, he felt at peace for the first time in as long as he could remember. He closed his eyes and said, "Thank you for a day of sobriety today. Help me to live soberly tomorrow. And let my life be marked by patience, tolerance, gentleness, kindness, love, integrity, discipline, self-control, and healthy thoughts. Help me not to be selfish, self-centered, or judgmental. Let me be slow to take offence and help me look for the joy that is all around me every day."

As he drifted off to sleep, Clint made a promise to himself to repeat that same prayer daily and to order his life around each item mentioned.

* * * * * * *

Over the next several weeks, Clint continued going to his Saturday morning AA meeting and also went to a several other meetings on weekday evenings. He also started attending meetings for sex addicts. To his surprise, he saw many of the same men there that were in his AA meetings. They exchanged shy grins and bumped fists.

One of the men he worked with became his sponsor in the Sex Addicts Anonymous meeting. Micah became his sponsor in AA.

Each Saturday morning before their meeting, he and Micah would go to the café and meet over a cup of coffee for about an hour. Clint would talk about his week. Micah would pull out the well-worn Big Book of AA that he kept in his hip pocket. He would read some from the book and then give Clint an assignment to do over the next week. The following week, they repeated the same routine. But from then on, their sponsor meetings would begin with Clint

showing Micah the assignment he had worked on throughout that week.

Little by little, Clint learned more about himself and was able to make the changes in his life he wanted to make. What a club! Clint thought about all he had picked up watching his friend, the changes he saw in him. He wanted all those qualities in his life. Now sober and solidly in recovery, he realized he could start moving toward each one of those qualities.

Chapter 14: Clint Puts It All Together

"Don't be afraid to go for what you want,
or what you want to be, but don't
be afraid to pay the cost."
~ Lane Frost

In September, the rain started. Thankfully, this was not going to be another Hill Country flood, but a gentle rain that lasted for a couple of days. The following week, it rained again—just another half of an inch or so. With the rain the water table came up and the water wells were all in full production.

At the breakfast meeting in mid-September, the foreman said, "I've been telling you guys that there were not gonna be any layoffs. And as far as a cattle sale goes—all we are doing is selling the calves and the older cattle as we do every year. The cattle will always be a part of this ranch. Your jobs are secure so long as you continue to give an honest day's work for an honest day's pay."

After the foreman left, one of the young hands Clint had given a hard time purposely bumped him as they were leaving the dining hall. As Clint turned to see who bumped into him, the young hand landed a powerful blow with his

fist on Clint's jaw. Clint's first reaction was to double up his own fist and pull back ready to even the score.

But before he could unload, he caught himself and relaxed his hand, and said, "I guess I had that coming. I've been ridin' you pretty hard. But I don't want to fight you. You've turned out to be a good hand. I think you're gonna fit in fine around here."

Micah, who had been watching the skirmish from a few feet away, grinned and motioned to Clint. "Come on Clint, we need to get started. We've got a long ride ahead of us." And with that, Clint and Micah headed to the corral. The rest of the men who were watching just shook their heads. They couldn't believe what they saw.

Clint had never backed down from a fight. They knew he could whip the kid. What they didn't know is why he didn't teach the youngster a lesson.

But Micah knew. Micah knew what was going on with Clint. Clint was finally on the road to recovery. He expected to see many changes in Clint's behavior over the next year. He also knew Clint's progress would not always be as startling as it was today. And he knew Clint would probably still be prone to lose his temper for a while. But he also knew if he stayed on his present course, Clint would

become the man he so wanted to be—a man not only other men looked up to, but a man that really was a man's man.

******

How does recovery happen? It starts with being tired of being under the influence, tired of not being capable of living a monogamous life, tired of wasting money chasing the gambler's dream of hitting it big. And in that moment, being willing to reach out for help. It begins with the recognition of being powerless over addiction.

Clint continued his evening prayer and meditation: "Thank you for a day of sobriety today. Help me to live soberly tomorrow. And let my life be marked by patience, tolerance, gentleness, kindness, love, integrity, discipline, self-control, and healthy thoughts. Help me not to be selfish, self-centered, or judgmental. Let me be slow to take offence and help me look for the joy that is all around me every day."

Each morning, as he prayed that prayer again, he would select each character quality he wanted in his life and think back to how he had succeeded or failed with regard to it the previous day. Then he would go to the next and then the

next. All the way through until he went through the entire list. He realized recovery was a long journey and there were no shortcuts to make it easier. But he also knew if he continued the road he was on, he was going to be the man he always knew he could be—a real cowboy's cowboy. Funny how his definition of what that meant had changed over the past year.

EPILOGUE

"For though the righteous fall seven times,
they rise again."
~ Proverbs 24:16

First light appeared as Clint left the dining hall. Sunrise in the Texas Hill Country can be breathtaking. The few clouds that dotted the sky would later be seen as an obstruction to sunlight. Now it was the backdrop to a bright orange sky that would fade too soon to just another sunrise. But for today, for this moment, the sky was a rainbow of hues from magenta to yellow, with the most vivid color being deep orange. No fruit was ever so colorful. Words couldn't describe the beauty that was displayed just for Clint. Or so it seemed to him.

Clint has now been completely sober for nine months. No alcohol. No drugs. No gambling. No sex outside of his marriage.

His wife has seen the changes he's made. She invited him back home three months ago on a trial basis and told him if the old Clint showed back up, he would have to go.

Clint was determined he was not going to go back to his old behavior. He knew promises came easily and had been broken before. What he told his wife this time was that he could promise that for today, he was going to live soberly and be faithful to her. He told her it was his goal to treat her as the queen of their home. Tomorrow, he would make the same promise to be sober and faithful and to treat her the way she deserved.

Clint contacted his attorney soon after his first AA meeting and said he wanted to go to trial as soon as possible. He pled guilty to driving under the influence. He was surprised to find the judge was someone he knew from his recovery meetings. Clint was given a three-month sentence but was allowed to work during the week and just had to spend each weekend in jail. The judge told him if he ever got another DUI, he would make it his mission to see that he went to prison.

As Clint worked the Steps of recovery, his sponsor said he needed to make amends to those persons he had harmed. Immediately his thoughts went to his wife and how he had hurt her with his continual cheating—sometimes flaunting it in her face. He realized she didn't deserve what he had done to her. It was not her fault, but it had messed up her life.

Working with his sponsor, Micah, it was determined the best starting place for making things right with his wife was for him to make a living amends. That not only meant he would never be unfaithful to her again, but he would treat her with the respect and gentleness she deserved. He was determined to spend the rest of his life being the very best husband he knew how to be.

Today their relationship is better than it's ever been. He's done with his running around. The party scene will have to get along without him. Every day, Clint is thankful for getting another chance with his wife and another chance at life.

There were many other amends he had to make. There was Tripp. And there were the many women he had hurt. His sponsor told him to write letters to each woman, read them to him, then destroy them, never having contact with former partners again.

The hardest was making amends to the husbands of his sex partners. He was sure more than once one of these men would take a swing at him, though no one did. But slowly and methodically, he went to each of these men who had found out about his behavior and told them that he had acted shamefully toward their wives. He took responsibility

for his actions and said the blame was all his because he had purposely seduced their wives.

For the husbands who didn't know of the affair he had with their wives, Clint wrote each a heart-felt letter and read it to Micah. Then he destroyed the letter, determined never to again act so dishonorably.

Some of those he made amends to were angry with him—especially some of the husbands. His sponsor reminded him his job was to just make the amends, not to control the response.

The amends did not hinge on the response of others. Each was a valid amends so long as he did what he needed to do to clean up his side of the street.

He also had to make amends to Micah. Hard feelings through the years, jealousy, sometimes not giving a good day of work, showing up hung over—all were behaviors that harmed his friend. Clint told Micah how he regretted his actions and how he was determined never to repeat any of them.

When Clint made his amends to his son Tripp, Tripp didn't want to talk to him. Before he walked away, Clint told him he had hurt Tripp's mom by being unfaithful and knew that his actions also hurt Tripp. He also told Tripp he set a

bad example for him with his drinking, using, and running around. Still Tripp was not at a point where he was ready to listen to the man who had wounded him so deeply.

******

Some months later, Tripp came to Clint and said, "Dad, I've noticed some changes in you. When I see you and mom together, both of you seem happier. And when I come over for Sunday lunch, you're not impatient like you used to be. You don't have your short temper any more. What's happened to you?"

Clint took a deep breath and silently gave thanks. "Well son, it's like this. About a year ago, a friend and I were moving cattle. I noticed some changes in his life and asked him what happened. He didn't tell me much. But one day he said he wanted to take me to a meeting. It was at that meeting where things began to fall into place for me, and my life changed. It has been a hard journey but a good one.

"When you think you are ready for a change—and to do the hardest work of your life—let me know and I'll take you to the same meeting. It'll change your life."

AFTERWORD

I love everything western. Most of all, I love the western culture. Cowboys may have a rough exterior but most I have known are true gentlemen with hearts of gold and integrity in abundance.

The quotes at the beginning of each chapter come from a variety of sources. The origin of most is unknown. Attribution is given when the source is known.

The H&F Ranch, Clint, Micah, and the other characters are composites of various places and people but are all fiction. The recovery journey, however, is true and is being played out in the lives of many other men and women every day.

Go to www.CowboyRecovery.com for more information about recovery. And for other traditional western novels set in the 1870s, visit www.TopWesterns.com. They are also set in Bandera, Texas on the H&F Ranch.

Much of the writing of *Clint's Journey Home* was done on various dude ranches in Bandera. A western atmosphere permeates these ranches so it was easy for my thoughts to be transported to a working cattle ranch during my writing retreats. I appreciate the hospitality of the following dude ranches that hosted me during these retreats: The Mayan Dude Ranch, The Dixie Dude Ranch, and the Silver Spur Guest Ranch. As you read about the H&F Ranch, you will recognize the dude ranch portion is a composite of these and other ranches I have either been to or researched.

Many of the characters in this book are composites of people I have met during writing retreats or got acquainted with many years ago. My first visit to a dude ranch was to the Mayan about thirty-five years ago. The Hicks family, who owns the Mayan, will see the resemblance of one of their employees from that time period to Jericho. There really was a ranch hand with dentures that spelled out T E X A S. And guests really did call him "Coffee Juice" after his habit of bringing early morning refreshment to them.

The jokes attributed to Jericho actually came from the crew of the Grand Canyon Railroad in Arizona. On a recent ride, we were treated to a train robbery and each of the "cow" jokes you read in this book.

As you visit Bandera, you will find the book to be a true representation of the city. The courthouse and courthouse rules are identical to what is described here. However, the various businesses described (such as the Cheer Up Saloon and the Better Days Motel) are composites places I have visited in Bandera as well as other places in Texas.

I would encourage you to plan a trip to Bandera soon and stay on one of the many fine dude ranches in the area. You will love the city, the western atmosphere, the people, and especially the hospitality.

I developed such affection for Bandera I began wondering what Bandera was like in the old west. After a significant amount of research, I embarked on writing a western novel set on the H&F Ranch in Bandera in the early 1870's. Before I knew it, I had a trilogy of western novels all around the same character, the Midnight Marauder.

If you enjoy western novels and liked reading about Bandera and the H&F Ranch, I would encourage you to check out the *Midnight Marauder* series on the following

websites: **www.TopWesterns.com** or on **www.Amazon.com**.

Roy Clinton

Getting Help Now

"Courage is being scared to death but saddling up anyway."
~ John Wayne

If you want what Clint and Micah have, you can get it beginning today. The first step for you is to admit to yourself that you can't do this alone. If you could, you would have done it by now. Recovery is not a matter of discipline, will, or strength. Recovery is a journey you don't take in isolation. You take it with other men and women who have been through things that are similar to what you have done.

Today, contact a Twelve-Step fellowship for the form of addiction you are facing. And if you have multiple forms of addiction, you will want to make contact with each relevant group. You must seek recovery for each form of addiction. In Appendix B, you will find a list of Twelve-Step fellowships for various forms of addiction. With each listing, you will find the contact information, so you can locate meetings near you.

Next, determine you are going to go to a meeting today.

This will be the beginning of a lifetime of attending meetings and working diligently on recovery. It's important to know you will never get to a place where you can pronounce yourself cured. But you can live a completely sober life beginning today.

As you go to your first meeting, make getting a sponsor in each fellowship your priority. The other men and women in the meetings will tell you how to get a sponsor. Your sponsor or sponsors, if you are in multiple fellowships, will serve as a mentor to you and will spend up to an hour with you each week to guide you in your Step work and in other aspects of your recovery.

Begin working the Steps of Recovery. Each Twelve-Step fellowship adapts the Steps to fit its particular form of addiction. Working the Steps is not the same as reading the Steps. Your sponsor will assign weekly homework for you around each Step. It will take you several months, perhaps a year or more, to work the Steps. Your sponsor will guide you and help keep you on track.

The thing your sponsor cannot do is provide you with motivation for recovery. If you provide the motivation and put in the hard work, your sponsor will guide your progress. Don't get impatient. Just commit to making regular progress.

If you have multiple forms of addiction and you can afford it, consider entering a treatment center that specializes in all forms of addiction. I have listed some of these in Appendix C.

Determine you are going to get help today. This is the day to begin recovery. This is YOUR day. May you find hope this day and ultimately freedom.

Appendix A:
Hope & Freedom Sex Addiction Recovery Resources

Recovery Programs at Hope & Freedom

Counseling Services
www.hopeandfreedom.com

713-630-0111

The main focus of the work at Hope & Freedom Counseling Services, and with the Certified Hope & Freedom Practitioners (**www.FindACHFP.com**), is in the area of sex addiction. However, we have also found many of the clients we treat realize their addiction has taken many forms. For recovery from addiction to be successful, all forms of addiction must be treated at once.

If you or someone you love engages in problematic sexual behavior, you might be a candidate for the recovery programs at Hope & Freedom or with a CHFP near you.

Lance and Wendy's Story

Lance entered recovery after Wendy discovered his acting out two years ago. He had done pretty well in recovery and attending a twelve-step meeting each week and meeting with his sponsor. As far as Wendy knew he had not acted out since entering recovery. She attended her own twelve-step meetings to help her understand how she had

missed the signs of her husband's acting out. She learned how to set boundaries as well as develop behaviors that helped her become more emotionally healthy in her recovery.

Although their recoveries were going well, their relationship continued to suffer. Wendy realized she was not trusting Lance and not sure that she had the complete truth about his past acting out behavior. They applied for admission to the Three-Day Intensive program at Hope & Freedom Counseling Services to rebuild their relationship and ensure they each remained on track with their recovery.

Three-Day Intensives

Three-Day Intensives are short but concentrated programs that focus on a particular aspect of recovery. They are not a "Three-Day Cure." There is no such thing. Rather, they are three days to do intensive recovery work in order to develop a solid foundation for recovery or to address a specific recovery need. During the Intensive, we will assess for other addictive behaviors. If a person suffers from multiple forms of addiction, it is crucial that all of them be addressed.

Hope & Freedom Counseling Services and CHFPs

offer a variety of Three-Day Intensives that are especially helpful for persons who live in geographical areas where sex addiction therapy is not available. These are particularly good for individuals or couples first entering recovery and are an ideal forum in which to deal with the crises that may have precipitated recovery. Intensives are also good for anyone who has not been able to maintain long-term sexual sobriety or has experienced a slip or relapse.

These are not the treatment choice for every individual or couple where compulsive sexual behavior is a factor. We accept fewer couples than apply for this treatment program. A number of factors may dictate that this is not the treatment option of choice.

Persons considering a Three-Day Intensive must be willing to work hard. They must be prepared to do whatever is necessary to stop the destructive behaviors related to sexual addiction and be willing to take extraordinary steps to restore their relationship. For the Intensive process to be successful, it requires couples to be willing to participate in the three-day experience, and also willing to work hard on rigorous assignments that are included each evening. In short, the Intensives we offer work best for highly motivated clients.

A prerequisite for participating in an Intensive is for both partners to be stable emotionally. Clients with untreated obsessive-compulsive disorder or bipolar disorder may not be good candidates for Intensives. After these disorders are stabilized with medication and therapy, they may be ready for the rigorous intensive process. Additionally, persons in danger of harming themselves are not appropriate for Intensives.

Couples who are approved for participation in Three-Day Intensives must make an unqualified commitment to stay in their relationship after the Intensive. This is crucial since disclosures typically reveal additional acting-out behaviors or details about them. This new information usually traumatizes the partner. When the pain associated with trauma starts, the typical response is to look to anything to stop the pain, including ending the relationship.

We ask partners to make a commitment to stay in the relationship for a minimum of twelve months after the Intensive, regardless of what the disclosure reveals. We ask sex addicts to double the commitment and to stay in the relationship a minimum of twenty-four months after the Intensive, regardless of their partner's anger or disappointment. Couples must agree to enter a contractual

agreement with that goal in order to be considered for participation in the Hope & Freedom Three-Day Intensive.

Couples who come to Intensives must be willing to devote their total effort to recovery for the full three days. This includes not conducting any "business as usual" during the Intensive. We also ask that contacts with home and family be minimized for the duration of the Intensive.

People interested in Intensives first must complete an online application before they are carefully screened to make sure they are appropriate for an Intensive and there is a reasonable expectation they will benefit from it. The content of the Intensive is customized to the specific needs of each client. Intensives are offered for couples as well as individually for men or women. However, if the client is in a committed relationship, we will only work with them as a couple, because successful recovery depends on both partners being involved in the recovery process. (Information and applications about Intensives may be found at www.HopeAndFreedom.com.) The following is a partial list of Intensives offered through Hope & Freedom Counseling Services as well as by Certified Hope & Freedom Practitioners.

Recovery Foundations Intensive

Recovery Foundations Intensives are designed for individuals and couples at the beginning of recovery and give participants a broad understanding of sex addiction and what is involved in recovery. There is an emphasis on understanding the origins of addiction and the factors that contribute to sex addiction.

These Intensives focus on integrating recovery routines into daily life, and beginning to reestablish trust in the relationship for couples. Sex addicts have the opportunity to take a polygraph exam to verify the disclosure of acting out is complete. Relapse prevention is also a significant focus. The Recovery Foundations Intensive culminates with each client drafting a Personal Recovery Plan.

Restoration Intensive for Couples or for Individuals

This Intensive is structured for couples where the sex addict has had some time in recovery but has had a slip or a relapse. Attention is given to understanding the cause of the relapse and preventing further relapses. A significant focus of this Intensive is dealing with the issue of trust. The couple is introduced to a process of trust rebuilding that requires commitment from each. It offers a high success

rate. A similar Intensive is offered for individuals who are not in a committed relationship.

Survivors Intensive for Couples or for Individuals

This Intensive is designed for couples where one or both partners have experienced significant past trauma. The trauma may go back to childhood, or may be connected to recent or current sexual acting out. These Intensives focus on the impact the trauma has had on the relationship, and has each partner begin the significant work needed to heal. A similar Intensive is offered for individuals who are not in a committed relationship.

Step-Down Intensive for Couples or for Individuals

This Intensive is designed as a step-down treatment for couples where the sex addict has just returned from inpatient treatment or from an extended intensive outpatient treatment facility. The emphasis is on life re-entry. Clients learn to identify and deal with daily triggers as well as learn new thought and behavior patterns to replace dysfunctional thoughts and behaviors. Relapse prevention and developing a Personal Recovery Plan round out the Intensive.

Special Topic Intensives

We offer special topic Intensives designed to fit specific clients' needs. These deal with a number of topics related to recovery such as multiple addictions where addiction is present for both husband and wife, recovery issues involving the family, or religious abuse.

High Profile Client Intensive

Individuals with high public profiles face special challenges entering recovery. If they go into a therapy office, they risk revealing their struggle with compulsive sexual behavior. To address this concern, we take the Intensive to the client. This Intensive is good for any high-profile person including senior executives, professional athletes, politicians, actors, broadcast personalities, and other celebrities. These are offered at a discrete location in Canada. Special arrangements can be made to have these Intensives in Europe or Asia. An extraordinary amount of effort is placed into guarding the identity of the client. The content is customized to fit the needs of the individual or couple. The location is chosen to allow for an extra buffer of anonymity not available for high-profile persons or celebrities who enter well-known treatment centers. More information

about High Profile Client Intensives can be found at **www.CelebritySexAddict.com**.

Additional Intensives are offered to meet the special needs of physicians and clergy. These Intensives are highly individualized to deal with the specific issues involved.

Preparing for Intensives

Clients preparing for Intensives are encouraged to make adequate preparations to ensure the success of their concentrated work. First, they are encouraged to spend time thinking about the events that have contributed to the need for the Intensive. For Intensives dealing with sexual addiction, it is important to make a complete, detailed, but confidential list of all acting-out behaviors. The more detailed and complete this list, the more effective the Intensive.

Clients who participate in a Three-Day Intensive are encouraged to take care of all business and family matters before coming to the Intensive and not conduct any business during the Intensive. Frankly, we have found that clients who conduct "business as usual" during an Intensive get limited benefit. For this reason, we strongly encourage clients to schedule an Intensive when they are able to devote

their full concentration to continuous therapy over three days.

To maximize the effectiveness of this time, we have the following stipulations:

- Leave cell phones, iPods, laptops, and other electronic devices off for the entire Intensive.
- Refrain from conducting business during the duration of the Intensive.
- Limit phone calls to one per day to check with family or to check on dependent children.
- Do not watch television or read newspapers during the Intensive.

The total focus of the three days is to concentrate on individual recovery and strengthen the relationship. Distractions must be kept to a minimum. Nothing should be allowed to hinder the important work that takes place during an Intensive.

It is beneficial for clients to stay an extra day or longer after the Intensive to process with their partner what they have learned and accomplished during the preceding three days. This time can be important as couples make plans to reenter life and consider how their restored relationship may

be different in the future.

Aftercare Program

A rigorous aftercare program is an important ingredient in any recovery treatment program. After the initial three days of work, we encourage couples to come back for periodic One-Day Aftercare Intensives. These are mini versions of a Three-Day Intensive. During Aftercare Intensives, couples receive a combination of individual and couples therapy. Aftercare Intensives are used to check up on recovery progress, and for the couple to learn additional tools of recovery and work on communication issues. A follow-up polygraph exam may be used to verify acting out has not recurred.

The first of these one-day follow-ups is scheduled three months after the initial Three-Day Intensive. They are scheduled every six months for an additional eighteen to thirty-six months, depending on the couple's needs. Thereafter, many couples opt to schedule an Aftercare Intensive annually as a checkup on the relationship and to monitor progress in recovery.

Additional information about Hope & Freedom Three-Day Intensives, as well as many free videos can be found at

the following website: **www.hopeandfreedom.com**. Dr. Magness can be contacted at the following email address: milton.magess@hopeandfreedom.com.

Special Note to Therapists

Our training program for therapists is called the Certified Hope & Freedom Practitioner (CHFP) training. In a typical year, one or two therapists who are already outstanding in their profession and have significant experience and training in working with sex addiction are selected for this training. Therapists who are interested in applying for the CHFP program can find an application at the following website: **www.hopeandfreedom.net**.

APPENDIX B: OTHER ADDICTION RECOVERY RESOURCES

Other Addiction Resources

Twelve Step Fellowships for Various Forms of Addictions and Compulsive Behaviors

Alcoholics Anonymous
www.aa.org

Castimonia (Christian sex addiction support)
www.castimonia.org

Cocaine Anonymous
www.ca.org

Crystal Meth Anonymous
www.crystalmeth.org

Debtors Anonymous
www.debetorsanonymous.org

Food Addicts Anonymous
www.foodaddictsanonymous.org

Gamblers Anonymous
www.gamblersanonymous.org

Infidelity Survivors Anonymous
www.isurvivors.org

Marijuana Anonymous
www.marijuana-anonymous.org

Narcotics Anonymous

www.na.org

Nicotine Anonymous
www.nicotineanonymous.org

Overeaters Anonymous
www.oa.org

Sex Addicts Anonymous
www.saa-recovery.org

Spenders Anonymous
www.spenders.org

Shopaholics Anonymous
www.shopaholicsanonymous.org

Workaholics Anonymous
www.workaholics-anonymous.org

Other Web-Based Resources
iRecovery Addiction Recovery Tracker

This iPhone™ and Android™ application is designed to keep track of recovery activities and plot the user's progress. The tracking process is also designed to be an encouragement to think about recovery daily. iRecovery works with any addiction and is also useful for helping partners track their progress.

Main Features

- Assigns recovery points to typical recovery activities
- Charts those activities and compares progress from week to week
- Users can add their activities and assign a point value for each
- User defined "Red Light," "Yellow Light," and "Green Light" behaviors
- "Contacts" button takes users to list of their Circle of Five contacts
- Recovery points can be customized to meet individual recovery plans as directed by counselor or therapist.
- www.RecoveryApp.com or in the Apple App Store or Google Play
- Users are able to compare their weekly recovery points

total, week by week, over the previous six months.

www.HopeAndFreedomU.com

This website has sex addiction recovery education that include streaming video courses.

Hope & Freedom Sex Addiction Video App

This smart phone app includes many free videos about sex addiction recovery. It is available for both iPhone™ and Android™. For more information, visit **www.RecoveryApp.com**.

APPENDIX C: TREATMENT CENTERS

Inpatient Addiction Treatment Centers

The following is a partial list of inpatient treatment programs that treat all forms of addiction.

Keystone Center
2000 Providence Ave.
Chester, PA 19013
www.keystonecenterecu.com
800-733-6840

The Meadows
1655 N. Tegner St.
Wickenburg, AZ 85390
www.themeadows.org
800-632-3697

The Ranch
P.O. Box 38
Nunnelly, TN 37137
931-981-9752

Pine Grove Gratitude Program
6051 U S Highway 49
Hattiesburg, MS 39401
www.pinegrovetreatment.com
888-574-4673

Santé Center for Healing
P.O. Box 448
Argyle, TX 76226
www.santecenter.com
800-258-4250

Sierra Tucson, Inc.
39580 S. Lago del Oro Parkway
Tucson, AZ 85739
www.sierratucson.com
800-842-4487

Do you love westerns? I'd like to invite you to enjoy the following series of western novels featuring the adventures of John Crudder now available at

www.TopWesterns.com or

www.Amazon.com

Here's how :

1) go to amazon.com
2) search for Roy Clinton
3) click on appropriate title
4) write a review

The review you write will help get the word out to others who may benefit.

– Thanks for your help,
Roy Clinton

Table of Contents

Other Books by Roy Clinton

Midnight Marauder

Return of Midnight Marauder

Revenge of Midnight Marauder

Midnight Marauder and the President of the United State

Love Child

Bad to the Bone

(Scheduled for release in early 2019)

These books and others can be found

on **www.TopWesterns.com** and **www.Amazon.com**.

Audio versions of the books can be found

on **www.Audible.com** as well as on iTunes.

 This is a work of fiction. Names, characters, businesses, places, events, and incidents are either the products of the author's imagination or are used in a fictitious manner. Any resemblance to actual persons, living or dead, or actual events is purely coincidental.

Published by Top Westerns Publishing

www.TopWesterns.com

For information, contact: info@topwesterns.com

Book Design by Teresa Lauer

Cover Design by Laurie Barboza, Design Stash Books DesignStashBooks@gmail.com

Edited by Sharon Smith

Printed in the United States of America

First Printing: January 2019

ISBN: 9781793207807

Lost

By Roy Clinton

NATIONAL BESTS

ROY CLINTON

LOST

"A skillful... modern-day cowboy tale..."
Kirkus Reviews